Jella: A V

Jella: A Woman at Sea

DEA BIRKETT

LONDON
VICTOR GOLLANCZ LTD
1992

To the officers and crew of MV *Minos*

First published in Great Britain 1992
by Victor Gollancz Ltd,
14 Henrietta Street, London WC2E 8QJ

The names of all characters have been changed.

A catalogue record for this book
is available from the British Library

ISBN 0 575 05125 6

Typeset at The Spartan Press Ltd,
Lymington, Hants
Printed in Great Britain by St Edmundsbury Press Ltd
Bury St Edmunds, Suffolk

. . . most seamen lead, if one may so express it, a sedentary life. Their minds are of the stay-at-home order, and their home is always with them – the ship; and so is their country – the sea.

Joseph Conrad

Oh, was there ever a sailor free to choose that didn't settle somewhere near the sea?

Rudyard Kipling

Crew List

Watches

First	2000–midnight
Middle	midnight–0400
Morning	0400–0800
Forenoon	0800–1200
Afternoon	1200–1600
Dogs	1600–2000

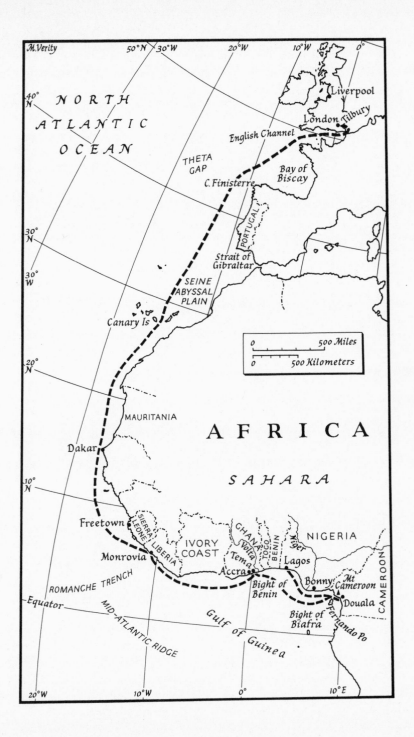

Part I

GOING ASHORE

Chapter One

No 12 Berth, Apapa Quays

LATITUDE 6°27′ NORTH, LONGITUDE 3°22′ EAST

In the shuttered building of the Nigerian Ports Authority, the emigration clerk counted the pages of my passport.

'One missing.' He was pleased by the originality of his complaint, accompanied by the burr of pages as he concertinaed through them with his thumb.

'No, there's not,' I insisted, quietly.

We began to count them again, slowly, together. He stared at my vaccination certificate.

'Just one mil typhoid?' He shook his head slowly. 'Not enough. You must pay twenty naira.'

'Just give him the money,' Sarah said, making no real effort to keep her voice down. 'Maybe it will prevent a typhoid outbreak on the streets of Lagos.'

I took out the bill. The clerk clicked his tongue and released a long coo through puckered lips. He flicked through the pages once again and handed the passport back over his desk.

'You're through,' Sarah stage-whispered. 'Now get out of here.'

I emerged on to the concrete glare of the quay. I hadn't expected the *Minos* to be right there in front of me. She looked so big. A solid black and iron-red vessel, ballooning over the dock and throwing a shadow which temporarily relieved the late afternoon sun. In her shade squatted rings of men, smoking, playing cards, watching and waiting for passing trade or a passing trick.

'Seester! Seester!' One of the squatting men waved a cellophane bag of bright green apples. 'You wan?'

'I no wan buy,' I shouted back. 'And I no be your seester.'

Strange, how you can hardly see any water in a dock. The ship seemed almost parked, like a lorry on dry land. From under her bow I couldn't see on board, just the human traffic passing up and down the gangway. The apple-seller was attempting to ascend to the decks, but there must have been someone checking at the top, for he came down quickly with the bag still clutched in his hand.

Apples had a high value in Nigeria. The military government had imposed strict import controls; apples were illegal commodities, a single fruit changing hands on the black market for the price of an average weekly wage. The penalty for smuggling was death.

The seller's apples shone an unnatural green – perfect, unbruised fruit, not musky and marked like the produce stacked high in West African markets. The cellophane bag in which they were displayed was proof of their value; even cellophane bags were items to be bartered. As he descended the gangway, he hissed through his teeth, a Nigerian whistle.

Sarah came out from the Ports Authority building, Simon Plunkett trotting behind her. I had been nervous of allowing Sarah to accompany me on board, knowing how she could, as they say in West Africa, 'Boss it'. Simon attempted to overtake her large, white, swaying body, draped in the deep blue *adure* cloth of the Yoruba women.

'This way, this way,' he waved arms which usually rested on his shipping agent's desk.

He had engaged three men – two young, one too old – to carry my luggage. They lifted the round brightly painted tin trunks on to their heads and walked in front of him up the gangway. I followed, holding on to the rope banister as the steel gangway swayed under us. There was a black man in a white boilersuit at the top, checking. Simon squeezed past Sarah.

'Sissay – I've brought Miss Birkett. She's sailing with you.'

Sissay nodded. He'd seen a lot. He'd seen, and known, white women.

'Where's the Captain?' Simon asked.

'Master dun go bridge.'

'Let's put you down in the bar for the moment, then,' Simon instructed with all the fake enthusiasm of a Boy Scout master, and commanded his strange retinue to follow – three porters, Sarah and me.

The officers' saloon was a lifeless, very oblong room. The curtains stayed pulled, as though to hide the fact that the windows were round, not square. Apart from the slight wooden lip edging the low tables, nothing disturbed this feeling of being on land.

Sarah lowered herself sedately into an orange plastic swivel chair with a tiny crescented back, the porters deposited my luggage about us, and we sat like queens surrounded by exotic offerings. Simon went off to find the Captain. His arms seemed lost without a pen in one hand, sheets of paper under the other, and flew about him.

'Back soon,' he smiled from the door, as his airborne limbs propelled him around the corner.

'Dreadful,' said Sarah with the last flash of his arm, raising inflated nostrils as if drawing in some terrible stench. 'Just. Like. A. Great. Big. Floating. British. Hotel.'

Sarah had been raised a colonial officer's daughter in East Africa. As an adult, she had returned to Britain, but found herself a stranger, and hurried back to the African continent. When we met she had been in Nigeria for five years, and her haughty well-bred Englishness had easily translated into that lazy air of indifference which West African women flaunt.

Sarah had thrown her worst insult: British – unbendingly British. There was nothing in this darkened bar to even hint that we were tied up with wrist-thick ropes to the banks of the West African coast. Photographs of ships – British ships – were screwed to each wall behind plastic frames. They were sister ships of the one we had just boarded, their names rooted in ancient Greek mythology reflecting nothing of the continent they served.

Not only the African continent was banished: there was no hint of a feminine presence in the brutal arrangement of the furniture. Four chairs with straight black metal legs and orange plastic padded seats stood around each wood-vinyl table, two one side, two the other, confronting each other as if ready for battle. The smell was stale: slightly of beer, slightly of smoke. There was a tiny bar, a large television, a video and a hi-fi system with cassettes lying around it. Sarah's soft, rounded body and *adure* cloth had brought something foreign and sensuous into this utilitarian male world, and it hung over the vinyl tables like a heady perfume.

A man appeared at the door, casually walked behind the bar,

opened the fridge and took out a beer. He pulled the ring from the can, walked towards us, and sat down.

'Which one of you's sailing with us?' He tapped out a cigarette, lit it and sucked with a strong hiss through smoke-stained teeth.

'I am,' I said.

'I'm the Sparks – the Radio Officer. Doug. Doug McWhirter.' He held out a hand. Each strand of Doug's hair was so straight and so thick it was as if he was wearing a wig made of wire. There were no curves on Doug, he was square and squat; his body could have been constructed out of a series of cardboard boxes covered in pink flesh. This was not at all the physique I had imagined of the deep-sea sailor. He shifted his heavy square glasses about on his nose as he spoke.

'Dea,' I said.

'Dea,' he repeated. 'Well, Dea.'

This was a statement in itself, not the start of one. That was it, I was here. He sucked again.

Another man appeared, tracing the same route across the brown carpet: door to bar, bar to fridge, can of beer, pop! pull off the ring. He leant over the bar, his large, sprawling figure folding over the counter. The sleeves of his white shirt rode up to reveal tattooed forearms. He was old, with grey and thinning hair, but still handsome in a rugged sort of way. Even in the few feet from the door to the bar he had managed to swagger.

'Which of you is the one?' he asked cockily. 'The Old Man said yesterday there was a female coming on board.'

Now this was my legendary seaman, physically battered but mentally unbowed, with a nasal Liverpool lilt.

'That's me,' I said perkily, trying to think of a joke.

I had deliberately dressed in my most feminine outfit. My sundress was red and blue flowers on a white background, gathered in at the waist. Sarah called it my Little English Number, but compared to her immense femininity my thin body seemed boyish.

'The Old Man will be in for a shock, then,' the legendary seaman chuckled. 'We thought you were one of those old dames who's been in the bush for years, missionary or something. Some kind of charity work for the blacks.'

'No,' I squeaked. 'I've been travelling.'

He was unimpressed.

'Travelled a bit myself,' he said. 'Been up and down and back and forth from this godforsaken continent for thirty years.' His trans-atlantic migrations were demonstrated by semaphore-like move-ments of tattooed forearms.

'I've applied for voluntary redundancy. Twenty-five thousand. No tax.' He toasted his cleverness with a chuckle. 'Do you know what it's like working with these people?'

He had turned on Sarah. I prayed she wouldn't say anything.

'Do you know what it's like?' he persisted. 'They even steal the tea bags, like the chimps in the ad.'

He, Jimmy Patterson, was Chief Steward – the only white man in the galley – so, he informed us, he if anyone should know.

'Want to know what I'll give you for breakfast on this ship?' Jimmy was enjoying himself. 'Coon-flakes,' and he drummed the bar with his fingers to applaud his own joke.

Doug sucked on his cigarette.

Oh God, Sarah, I prayed.

Sarah sat, stolid, with a smile so insulting, so disdainful.

'Really?' she said, as if utterly fascinated by some new and exotic dish. I dreaded she might just dare ask him for the recipe.

'I'd better be going,' and she steadily raised herself from the swivel chair. I had always been awed by how Sarah held her head firm on a strong neck, proud in her largeness.

'Coming to see me off,' she ordered rather than asked.

We left the two men finishing their beers.

At the top of the gangway, Sarah kissed me lightly on both cheeks.

'These men seem *dreadful*,' she breathed. 'You'll be all right if you just keep away from them. Treat it as a great big floating hotel,' and she threw her arms out at the imaginary luxury complex, and wobbled down the gangway.

'Ha!' said Jimmy triumphantly, who had sneaked up from the bar behind us and watched the parting. 'Gone!'

Sarah's indigo dress had already blended in with the crowd. Soon the gangway would be raised, and I would be severed from Sarah and the land. The thought made my face twitch helplessly. I tried to regain control by clamping my lips in a ridiculous smile, but a single tear was already trickling slowly down my cheek. The legendary seaman and I stood looking at each other for a few seconds, my mouth and cheeks horribly distorted, before he decided he had to do something to prevent him having a blubbering female in a flowery dress on board.

'Come on, then! I've got some work to do in the office!' he cheered, and led me from the deck back inside the belly of the ship.

The purser's office, Jimmy explained, was where he did his business. I could call him the Purser, the Chief Steward, the Catering Officer – it was all the same thing nowadays. There used to be one man for each job, but now everything was rolled into one man. That man, his pointed finger indicated, was Jimmy.

Jimmy came from Liverpool, and his home town had sent him, as many of its working-class boys, to sea. That was thirty-seven years ago, and Jimmy had been fifteen. He had been a captain's steward when the captain had had a steward, an assistant steward when there had been assistant stewards, and a chief cook when the chief cook had been British. Now, like the rest of the eleven ratings on board, the chief cook was a Kru from Sierra Leone.

When Jimmy first went to sea, at four o'clock every afternoon, with the exception of Sundays, a senior officer would have been served with a vodka and lime from a silver tray by his personal steward. Jimmy had been that steward, and wanted to be that officer. But by the time Jimmy became that officer there were no more vodkas and lime, no more silver trays. He had carried his beer with him from the bar; he used the can to point my way towards the purser's office.

I had expected to find a business-like room, order books standing neatly along the back of a desk, notes tucked into the edge of a blotter: 'Order a crate of oranges at Banjul'. But the chatter as we approached the door embossed PURSER told me it was a different kind of business.

The small room contained two men in ill-fitting suits and crooked ties which were strangling them in nooses of sweat; the apple-seller, who had somehow managed to get past Sissay; and his friend who, seeing me, drew up a baggy waxprint sleeve to reveal a wiry black arm hanging with ivory bangles. A well-dressed woman, wrapped in George cloth, greeted Jimmy, the elaborate lace distinguishing her as a Yoruba woman of wealth.

'Barbara,' Jimmy welcomed. 'Everything OK?'

Barbara was the shipping line's fix-it woman. A professional smuggler – one of the best – she bypassed customs controls through a combination of charm and 'dash'. She smuggled goods in for the Kru men on board and goods out to the shipping line's white agents on shore.

As Chief Steward and keeper of the keys to the walk-in refrigerators, Jimmy was the benevolent dispenser of Britishness to these stranded expatriates. That morning, he had handed Barbara boxes of frozen pizzas, fishfingers and sausages. These were considered illegal imports by Nigerian customs, but to the white agents they were luxuries, and stirred fond memories of a home in the supermarketed suburbs. In daily battle against the heat and disease and people surrounding them, they greeted the packaged food like a besieged army would its Red Cross rations. Simon Plunkett's wife Jenny and seven-year-old daughter would be the beneficiaries of the smuggled pizzas.

Barbara presented Jimmy with the bill:

> Taxi – 8 Naira
> Police – 10 Naira
> Nigerian Security Organisation – 25 Naira
> Customs – 15 Naira
> Commission – 30 Naira
>
> TOTAL 88 Naira. Thank you.

Jimmy read it out loud, unconcerned by the two men in suits, officials of the Nigerian Ports Authority who were waiting for their dash.

'What's this twenty-five naira for? You paid the NSO fifteen last time,' he challenged.

The Nigerian Security Organisation was the notorious bully-boy wing of the police department, established by Decree Number Sixteen for 'The prevention and detection of any crime against the security of the country'.

Would Jimmy ask Barbara for the proof of a receipt? 'Twenty-five Naira. Received with Thanks. Signed Chief Interrogator, Nigerian Security Organisation.'

The purser's office became, in that moment, a microcosm of a Nigerian market. Barbara wound and unwound her wrapper skirt, flapping it about her; wound and unwound her headtie, tucking it in like a turban around her short hair. This was the sign language of the market women, bargaining, continually rearranging their clothing until, wrapper tied tight and headtie securely fastened, a deal was struck.

Jimmy, restrained in the long white shorts and short-sleeved white shirt of his tropical uniform, called upon their mutual acquaintances, their long and beneficial friendship, his loyalty as a customer, his fondness for her as a woman.

'Would I lie to you?' she retorted. 'I know you since you no more than captain's steward!'

Jimmy reached for a bottle of Johnnie Walker, poured out four portions and sealed a deal at seventy naira, the price he had always known he would have to pay, the price Barbara had always known she would have to accept. It was the moment the port officials had been waiting for; he passed them each a tumbler.

'Oga Jimmy. Master Jimmy,' they toasted with respectful grins.

The *Minos* had been docked at No 12 Berth at Apapa Quays, Lagos, for ten days. Behind doors marked PURSER, MASTER, and CHIEF OFFICER, negotiations had stretched late into the night, over tumblers of whisky and shrouded in cigarette smoke, to engage gangs of shoreworkers, stevedores, and transport on the wharf.

A 21,000 deadweight tonnage 'combo' cargo vessel, the *Minos* had been designed for the general West African trade. Unlike other more specialised vessels, she could carry loose break-bulk cargo as well as containerised goods, or a full cargo of either. Her builders had advertised her as a MODERN MULTI-PURPOSE SHIP DESIGNED FOR COMPLETE FLEXIBILITY, but they had not reckoned with West Africa. Although she could be self-loading, with her nine derricks capable of lifting up to sixty-five tons, she needed shore gangs to work her and forklift trucks to shift the loose cargo.

When I came on board, hatches number two and five still had to be discharged of salt, and 3,800 bags of raw cocoa beans, 2,832 cartons of cocoa butter unitised in pallets, and 132 empty containers had to be loaded, bound for the *Minos*'s home port of Liverpool. That morning the tally clerks had not turned up for the first shift, and three gangs of labourers had been lying idle for two hours. There had been no forklift trucks available to shift cargo. The full consignment of cocoa had still not arrived. Then, just as the congestion on the wharf cleared and the cocoa was delivered to the quay, it had rained and the hatches had had to be closed. When, in the mid-afternoon, one of the shore gang was accused of breaking the seal on a container and pilfering the contents, his fellow workers had staged a sit-down, and work had stopped again.

Simon Plunkett, with multiple copies of the completed cargo manifests now occupying his hands, came to collect me from the purser's office.

'The Captain is in his cabin expecting you – let's go.'

Jimmy, deep in negotiation with the Ports Authority officials, now with Barbara on his side, didn't notice me leave.

When we reached the door marked MASTER, Simon knocked. An old man answered.

The business of shipping is not the same as the business of sea-faring. They are two quite distinct professions. Simon Plunkett was a shipper; the Captain was a seafarer. Only briefly meeting when the ship is in port, they shared no common ground. Shipping is conducted in offices, on land, by those whom seafarers disparagingly call 'college boys'. Seafaring is the skill of handling and mastering a ship, on the ocean. In the shipping-line office at Apapa, the captain may be cowed by a company clerk. But on board it is the company clerk who flounders.

'Miss Birkett, sir,' Simon introduced me like a page boy announcing a guest to a banqueting suite. Then he shuffled off.

The old man stepped aside and ushered me in, pointing to a chair. He was solid rather than fat, and of a good height. If he had had to enter his colour on a passport application, the most accurate descrip-tion would not have been white, but pink. The skin around his chin and neck was loose with age and wobbled slightly as he spoke.

'Drink?' he said.

'Yes, thank you.' I sat down.

'Gin?'

'Lovely.'

The old man turned his back on me and opened a cabinet whose modest wood-vinyl exterior hid an inside constructed entirely of mirrors, in which were reflected infinitesimal rows of Beefeater bottles. Several *National Geographic* magazines were stacked perfectly flush at one end of the long coffee table. *The Army of the Caesars* lay open, cover out, on top of a giant television. Through a half-open door, I saw into his sleeping quarters. On the bedside table, a bottle of Old Spice aftershave carried a picture of a sailing galleon.

'Thought you must be a missionary. But you're young,' the Captain sniffed, handing me a glass. My age seemed to be taken as a personal insult to him, a deliberate trick on my part.

'Had no idea what you were,' he added. No personal pronouns littered the Captain's speech; he embodied his ship, his officers, his crew.

He padded up and down, turning over this statement.

'Used to get wives travelling with us quite a bit. Not any more.' He gave a curt summary of women who had invaded his masculine world. A single man himself, he didn't exactly approve.

'I've been travelling in West Africa,' I offered. 'I've been following the route of Mary Kingsley. She came here in the 1890s. I wanted to return as she did, on a cargo vessel.'

'Mary Kingsley. Ah.' There had been a ship named the *Mary Kingsley*, he told me. On a voyage to West Africa in a severe equinoctial gale, a locomotive she was carrying had broken adrift from her deck and sunk to the bottom of the ocean. Now it all made sense. First Mary Kingsley the person. Then *Mary Kingsley* the ship. Now me.

'Ah,' he nodded, as if remembering something in the distant past. 'Better put you next to me. Never know,' and he picked up the phone, located Simon Plunkett, and gave him instructions to have my baggage moved from a spare cabin on the officers' deck to the one next to his own.

'Young,' he shouted down the receiver. 'Never know.'

The door on the cabin next to the Captain's had a small sign with PILOT embossed on it. I sat on the bed and began to unpack. I had wound my clothes around the possessions I had gathered on my journeys: a terracotta water pot, a hand mirror framed with battered Fanta cans, a Fulani horse bridle of uncured leather. Already the leathery smell was invading the cabin. When I had haggled cross-legged in Kurmi market in the Old City of Kano, the crude circles of metal for blinkers strung to the bit with torn strands of multi-coloured ribbon had seemed to capture the dignity of the Durbar horsemen. Here, amongst the same orange vinyl furniture as in the bar, the bridle just looked tatty. I buried it back into the tin trunk and pushed the trunk to the back of the cupboard. The colour and chaos of West Africa had no place in this nice clean cabin, and I was glad.

After four months in West Africa, I was travel weary. I had climbed the rocks of Rano to discover iron-age forges, bartered with Yoruba market women, and eaten the Fulani's sour yoghurt and millet, *fura de nunu*, from carved calabashes. Now I craved familiar things. I didn't want any more new experiences; I wanted a time and a place in which I could slowly and gently re-adjust to my life in Britain.

I had been wandering around West Africa looking for clues, insights and memories of Mary Henrietta Kingsley, a Victorian woman traveller who had trekked through 'the white man's grave' almost a hundred years before I had arrived. It had been a futile task, and I hadn't found her anywhere. To the people I met on the way, my quest made no sense at all. Why was I coming to West Africa in search of a tourist who had left nearly a century ago? I said she was my great-great aunt, hoping this might help, but this only provoked another question – if you have family, why are you travelling without them? Why, everyone wanted to know, are you alone?

When I heard about another young British woman alone in Nigeria, who was reputed to wear Yoruba dress, absurd earrings, and a most disdainful air, I set about seeking her out. After a four-hundred-mile journey along a potholed road in the back of a 'flying coffin', the shared taxis used as public transport, I arrived at her home in Ile-Ife to be told she had gone to a film on the university campus. I went to wait for her outside the cinema, dishevelled and exhausted.

The first time I saw Sarah's wonderfully large body, it was strolling out of that cinema in the midst of a riot. Sarah made her way slowly through the angry crowd, parting them with great sweeps of her arms, wrapped in a wealth of waxprint cloth like a big market madam. From her ears were hanging two tiny plastic helicopters.

Riots were not uncommon in Nigerian cinemas. If the audience found a film offensive they would first shout at the screen, then start clapping, and lastly get up to leave. The riot began when they demanded their ticket price back from the box-office clerk, who refused. Nigerian box offices were built like bunkers and heavily protected with wire grills.

It was Sarah who had suggested I return by ship. If Mary Kingsley had given me reason to wander around West Africa, why didn't I also travel back as she had done? The shipping line on which the Victorian spinster had sailed still worked the British–West African route. I listlessly agreed that the voyage might provide some of the insights which had so far eluded me. It also seemed an ideal way of avoiding the culture shock of flying from Lagos to London in under half a day. A sea voyage would be the least taxing way to travel home.

The shipping line's office was along Wharf Road in Apapa. I went to meet the managing director, just arrived in Lagos from Liverpool on business for a few days. I explained how I had been following the route of a Victorian woman traveller and wanted to sail back with the same line which had taken her home.

The MD was not at all sure that this was a good idea. He leant back in his chair, buried his chin in his neck, and pressed his fingertips together as if to pray.

'What if you get sick?'

I shrugged my shoulders. I had never been on a cargo vessel, and had no idea how I would cope with weeks at sea.

'You'll be the only woman on board.' He raised his eyebrows and considered me with paternal concern.

But for this I had an answer. 'So was Mary Kingsley.'

'We don't take passengers any more . . . ' he said, but I could tell he was already coming around. He leant forward in his chair and let his fingers slip between each other, clasping his hands together, ' . . . but as long as the Captain's happy with the arrangement, it's all right by me.'

For the most unromantic of reasons – insurance purposes – I had to be signed on as a member of crew. I had no ambition to be a sailor, but the MD had made it clear that it was the only way I would be allowed to travel.

On board the *Minos*, in the cabin marked PILOT, the MD's

warnings seemed a mere formality. This was a long way from Africa and all the surprises it had sprung on me. I was looking forward to an idle voyage home in a safe, undemanding, British ship. I shook out my clothes vigorously. Dinner, I had been informed, was at 1900 hours.

I entered a room full of men in uniform at ten past seven, still in my Little English Number, and headed for the spare chair on the Captain's table next to the Sparks, Doug. At the end of each of the two tables stood a black man dressed entirely in white. As I sat down, one of these men offered me a white card typed up with a menu. The Captain, already on his main course ('York Ham and Cauliflower Natural' I read), nodded my arrival. The other men went on eating in silence.

'Hello,' a squeak emerged from my mouth in reply to the Captain's nod. Simon Plunkett had warned me – a woman on board might not be greeted with enthusiasm.

'Funny buggers. Seamen,' he'd said. 'Never really know what they're thinking. They're unpredictable. Bit like Africans.'

The Captain had to explain my presence to his men, but this captain was not a man who explained things; he simply stated the facts. He lowered his spoon to a strangled cough.

'Miss Birkett is sailing with us. She's been travelling in Nigeria.'

The black man hovered above me. I glanced at the menu. It seemed indecipherable. 'Eskimo Nell'? At the top, next to the logo of an anchor, was typed 'Apapa Quays, Lagos'.

'This is Eskimo Nell.' The bearded man sitting opposite me pointed at a round ball of meat swimming in a reddish pool on his plate.

'Yes, please,' I flicked a weak smile at the waiting steward.

'York Ham, master?' he asked.

'Yes, please.'

'Ice cream, master?'

'Lovely.'

Mostly middle-aged, all white, the officers framed the white tablecloth cluttered with silver cutlery. A portrait of the Queen in a splendid white sequinned dress hung above them. There were places set for each of the eleven officers. The Chief Engineer ('Chief'), First Mate ('Mate'), Radio Officer ('Sparks'), and the

Chief Steward sat at the Captain's table. The junior officers' table was for the Second, Third, Fourth and Electrical ('Lecky') Engineers, the Second and Third Mate, and two Mexican cadets. The Sierra Leonean crew (the boatswain, the cook, two stewards, five sailors and two engine-room men), were eating somewhere else, something else, in their parallel but separate life on board.

The conversation, if there had been any, had halted since my late arrival. It started up again. The *Minos*'s starboard quarter had been clipped by a Dutch vessel backing out of the Ro-Ro Terminal, and her stanchions had been damaged. Doug had tried to make radio contact, but no answer was received and the Dutch ship had proceeded from the harbour as if nothing had happened. The officers chatted about the worries in port, ignoring the Captain ploughing steadily through his food, and ignoring me.

'When will be sailing, sir?' The man with Eskimo Nell addressed the Captain.

'Scheduled for 2130,' he replied.

A smile shivered along the row of male faces. By this time tomorrow, we would be at sea.

Chapter Two

At Sea

LATITUDE 6°27' NORTH, LONGITUDE 3°22' EAST
TO LATITUDE 3°53' NORTH, LONGITUDE 9°31' EAST

The pilot came on board, the ropes were cast off, the ship was swung seawards, the unreliable buoys in Lagos Lagoon were dodged, a bearing was taken from Dejection Jetty, and the pilot was lowered back over the side into a launch before we cleared the harbour and were full away to sea. The Captain instructed Sissay to steer 137 degrees, across the Bights of Benin and Biafra, bound for Douala.

MV *Minos* worked about me while I slept in my cabin. The Third Mate handed over to the Second on the bridge at midnight, and the First came on duty at four for Morning watch.

When I awoke the whole room was moving. It was only a very gentle sway but enough to defeat any attempt at organising my thoughts for longer than a few seconds at a stretch. So I gave myself simple orders: Get washed. Get dressed. I squatted in the cool white hollow of the bath and threw cups of water over me from the toothbrush mug, washing West African style.

Out on deck, the early sun tussled with the haze. I hung over the rail. European knowledge of West Africa had come from the water. In the fifteenth century an ambitious Portuguese sailor named Bartholomew Dias stumbled across the south-west coast of Africa while seeking sea routes to Asia. Where water was, Europeans could go too. Soon they began to chart the rivers of the new-found continent – their breadth, their depths, the force of their flows. These were the motorways of Africa, the highways to the eldorados of the interior.

For three centuries, expeditions returned defeated. The River Ogun, named after the Yoruba god of war, flowed from the north bank of Lagos Lagoon. Its rapid downward currents and shallow beds made it impassable to any but the large flat-bottomed dugout canoes, balanced so finely no European had been able to master them. Victorian technology – the invention of flat-hulled, sturdy steel steamers – allowed the interior to be pierced for a brief period only. Within sixty years, the Nigerian Ports Authority had become the new dam to European advancement, demanding 'dash' before vessels could get pilotage up through the confusion of inland creeks.

Wave, Main, Sea, Briney, Ocean. I tried to remember all the words for water. Everywhere, I thought. If the Nigerian coast was forty miles on our port beam, I couldn't see it.

Puddle, Pond, Lake, River. I had always lived by the water. My grandmother, who worked in a toyshop in the Fulham Road, took me through Bishop's Park on Sunday lunchtimes where boxed hedges rimmed the Thames. When we went to visit, my father awarded sixpence to the first to see the river. In the back of the car, my brother and I fought for the prize.

We lived further upstream in the new suburbs of Surrey. One year our house was flooded, and my best friend Julia Hatherall and I flashed torches at each other from the islands of our bedroom windows. Floating army tanks, called Ducks, delivered two loaves of Sunblest and three pints of milk to each family.

Even then, when the man two doors up rowed along our street, turned right at the sign for East Molesey, looked back and waved to me hanging out of the top window, I was not afraid of the water. We walked beside it most weekends. It licked the banks. I hit it with big sticks and threw things into it. Dogs swam in it. Cyclists pedalled along beside it.

That was before the Thames Barrier was built out of vast shell-shaped steel hollows to catch the rising waters. Less engineered devices stemmed ambitious tides. Along the towpath, the banks were reinforced in places by planks of wood wedged upright into the mud. Closer into town, concrete pavements were laid right to the edge, confidently grey and dusty although bordering the broad ribbon of silty water. The river was framed by human activity, formed by manbuilt barriers.

But the ocean. Everywhere. I sniffed, and hurried back inside the ship. The ocean was far too large to contemplate so early in the morning.

*

I met the man with Eskimo Nell by the heat lamps warming the scrambled egg and smoked haddock on the serve-yourself breakfast counter, piling fried bread on to a full plate.

'Morning.'

'Morning.' We nodded at each other.

The Captain was already in his place at the head of table, sipping his cereal. He ate cornflakes as if they were soup, tipping the bowl away from him, dipping a silver spoon into the liquid, raising a stiff forearm, then sucking loudly through suctioned lips, barely letting his mouth touch the spoon. This movement was executed in a slow military fashion, with a quick jerk as the food approached his bent head, as if the Captain was about to salute the officers gathered before him. All his food was eaten in this manner, and from a bowl. Cereal, smoked fish, scrambled egg, 'York Ham and Cauliflower Natural', sat safely within the hollow of a dish, in preparation, I imagined, for a storm.

'Lovely morning,' he announced to myself and the man with Eskimo Nell as we dragged out chairs from under the white tablecloth.

Each table was ordered hierarchically. The Captain was flanked by the Chief Engineer and the First Mate, a homely looking man of average build who seemed neither disturbed nor interested in my arrival at the dining table. Doug the Sparks sat at the other end, where there was also a place for Jimmy the Chief Steward, although he never took it. I sat opposite his empty chair, between the Mate and Doug.

The man with Eskimo Nell was Roger Bird, Chief Engineer. If the officers with places at the Captain's table had been lined up in order of height, Roger would have appeared first, quickly followed by the Chief Steward Jimmy, then the Mate, with Doug a good way behind. If, on the other hand, the order had been determined not just by inches tall but a measure of the seaman's presence, the Chief Steward would easily have outranked the lean, lanky Roger. Although Roger sported a sailor's dark, short, pointed beard, it was as if he wore it as a disguise, for he was not moulded by the sea. He had first practised his trade of engineer in his native landlocked Shropshire, for a local engineering company, before going to sea. He had the weaseled look of a man who had to execute delicate work with too-large hands.

'Better put you to work too,' stated the Captain, staring at his tilted bowl.

He could only mean me. There was a titter among the men.

'Steersman. First watch.' The Captain instructed me to join the Third Mate on the bridge at 2000 hours.

I spent my first morning at sea lying under the blankets in my air conditioned cabin, wallowing in memories of the land I had just cast off. Africa, for all its infuriating unpredictability, was a funny, joyful, human place and life on board the *Minos* seemed dull and colourless in comparison. I recalled sleeping on verandas in the interior, enveloped in the cool smoothness of a single white sheet. The north of Nigeria was bush bordering on desert, littered with scruffy shrubs which looked dead even when alive. All colour was muted by the dust and heat, so the shrubs seem as if pencilled on to the grey-brown earth. Men moved around in pale blue rigas; long tent-shaped garments reaching to the ground with slits for their arms.

It had been harmattan – the two months before the rains – and oppressively hot. Harmattan arrives as a fierce easterly wind from the Sahara carrying the nomadic Tuareg traders with their wares for Kurmi market, escaping from the heat, and with them clouds of desert dust suspended in the air like fog. Going for a walk was like swimming; you could feel the atmosphere part before you. It sucked the fluid from everything – your skin, your eyes, your throat.

A two-day train journey away, down in Lagos, harmattan came as a welcome relief from the extreme humidity of the riverine coast. The wind evaporated the moisture and brought the temperature of the earth down with such beneficial effects that it was nicknamed 'the Doctor'. I didn't even need a sheet to keep me cool at nights. I slept in my wrapper.

Through Sarah, I had an introduction to the health correspondent of the local *Guardian* newspaper, and I had stayed in her Lagos flat at 1004, the vast estate on Victoria Island named after the number of housing units it contained. The three enormous central blocks of 1004 towered over Five Cowrie creek.

One in four Africans is Nigerian, and one in four Nigerians lives in Lagos. The effect of this has been to rob the town of the original reason for its growth and prosperity – it was a major port. Now buildings swell over the water as land is continually reclaimed from the swamps. Even the shipping line's old office across the Marina has been cut off from the water. Less than thirty years ago, ships docked right in front of the building, loading heavy cargoes of palm kernels, cocoa beans, groundnuts, rubber and timber from the warehouses. Now what had been the wharf was reclaimed as a car park for city workers.

The Lagoon often seeks revenge for being overrun by the city. Lagos is nowhere more than twenty-one feet above sea level, and water seeps up between the foundations of modern apartment blocks and floods newly laid roads. In the rainy season, the streets in the middle-class district of Surulere are awash.

Bar Beach stretches out from the east of town at the start of a forty-mile steep sandy seafront, on which breaks a heavy surf. Despite its treacherous undercurrent, Bar Beach used to be a popular place for Lagosian families and lovers to picnic and bathe away from the crowds. Then the armed robbers arrived. It was an ideal spot for a robbery; no one could hear the gunshots and the screams for help amidst the roar of the crashing surf.

Restless and enticed by the prospect of a little luxury, I had moved from my couch in 1004 to a double-bed divan in the home of the Second Secretary of the Irish Embassy, another of Sarah's strange assortment of contacts. The wrought-iron gate of his compound had automatically clicked open at the sight of my white face in the back of the yellow taxi. That night there was to be a big party in honour of the arrival of the man sent from Dublin to relieve the current Second Secretary at the end of his three-year posting.

Exchange between Ireland and Nigeria is of a cerebral nature, and most of the guests were men and women of the cloth. Sisters of Our Lady of Apostles, fathers of St Patrick's Missionary Society, and brothers of the Society of African Missions sipped minerals or stood with whiskies in their scrubbed pink hands.

A round, red-faced priest in a heavy, dragging habit floated up to me.

'Father Heineken-don't-laugh,' he said as if the whole phrase was his name, holding out a firm hand. 'Padre to the port.'

'Oh, how interesting. How long have you been here?'

It was the sort of party where you stood up, balanced a drink, and offered polite conversation.

'Thirty years.' He took another gulp from his glass. 'Thirty goddamned years,' and floated off.

A Lebanese Catholic ('One of our converts!' a nun had cheered) with an Irish wife told me with a flourish that he was 'into Import–Export' and jotted down his three addresses – 'in case you need to get in touch' – PO box, home, and office in Bombay Crescent, Apapa.

'Yes, three! I've got three!' he laughed unprompted, throwing back a bald, brown pate, in case I hadn't realised the full wealth of his residences.

'Miscegenation! Mis-ceg-en-a-tion! What the Catholic church needs is a black Pope!' Father Heineken was reeling his way towards us. The sisters, fathers, brothers, and the incoming Second Secretary kindly lowered their eyes as if asking the Almighty to forgive the poor Padre.

Outgoing Second Secretary Michael Shaughnessy, our official host, darted among the seated ladies. 'Such a *nice* man,' one of the sisters whispered.

After three days in the Second Secretary's compound, I discovered that Michael Shaughnessy was not so fond of himself. He was continually shocked by the blunt orders he heard emanating from his thin lips. He hated the strut his compact, bird-like body had come to assume. Our conversations around the dining-room table tended towards the topic of 'The brutalisation of the white man in a black land' as three-course meals were served by the Second Secretary's cook Grant, who lived with his family in the two-room concrete-block boy's quarters in the back garden of the Second Secretary's compound. I never discovered how Michael, who I thought would have been much more suited to working in a university Ethical and Religious Studies Department, came to be a neo-colonial diplomat.

One night the incoming Second Secretary, Patrick Kavanagh, joined us for dinner at the big table. He was to inherit Michael's house and possessions, most importantly the electricity generator and Grant. 'Perks' the new Second Secretary would have called them.

'I've heard very good things about you, Grant,' the younger man said to the elder, like a boy playing at being a general. 'Very good indeed.'

Patrick Kavanagh knew what he wanted and what his role in this country would be. He was a happy, plump, married man. He hoped to bring a family feel to the post, an approachable face to officialdom, he said, avoiding with his eyes but pinpointing with his words, Michael's tense, slight body.

'The kids would only come if they could go to school on a camel,' he chuckled, downing Michael's wine. 'Told them they could, of course.'

'You're welcome to stay any time, any time,' he gestured to me over the roast, offering with a sweep of his heavy arm the sideboard of Waterford crystal glasses, the silver-plated cutlery, the polished oak extendable dining-room table, and the hatch through to the kitchen where Grant cooked, as if bachelor Michael had already left and Patrick Kavanagh and his family had moved in.

'You won't much like what you become.' Michael's warning was drowned in his successor's insistent 'umms' of admiration for the rack of lamb.

I had met Sister Elizabeth of Our Lady of Apostles – the first congregation of nuns to arrive in Nigeria – at the party. She had invited me to go and visit her at St Mary's Secondary School in Broad Street, the old Brazilian colony, where she taught Moral Instruction.

'I was just talking to my Class Six students on the evils of this time,' she said walking towards me across the playground. 'The executions on account of the drugs.'

That month Miscellaneous Offences Decree Twenty had been implemented, stipulating the death penalty for a wide range of offences, from illegal oil bunkering to peddling narcotics. Three women and six men had been tied to oil drums on Bar Beach and shot by firing squad. The men had exchanged small amounts of foreign currency, ten or twenty dollars, on the black market. The women had smuggled cocaine. Nineteen-year-old Sola Oguntayo had given birth in detention. Twenty-one-year-old Gladys Iyamah was already a mother of three severely crippled children; she had hoped the money earnt by smuggling would buy them a miracle cure. The women had hidden packets of white powder in what the Nigerian press coyly referred to as their 'sacred recess', 'warehouse', 'parking space', or 'diplomatic bag'. They had been strip-searched.

I told Sister Elizabeth how I had been four hundred miles away in south-eastern Nigeria when the first execution took place, and some days later was drawn by a crowd in Calabar's central market.

'Customer! Customer! I beg come buy now, my friend!' the seller shouted. People emerged from the crowd clutching small cards, like Mass cards. I pushed forward, hoping for a bargain.

The young man fanned out the pictures as if displaying a deck of cards. One black and white photograph showed a body held up by ropes wound around an oil drum, the head dangling down. A few were of young men bound but still alive, staring at the point where the guns must have been.

'One naira. You give me five naira, I give you six snaps,' the seller beamed.

I pushed out through the flutter of notes.

Later that same day, I had visited the home of the Moderator of the Presbyterian Church of Calabar. A kind, soft-spoken, elderly gentleman, he had taken me to see the grave of the missionary Mary Slessor, a friend of Mary Kingsley.

'I enjoy helping people. That is part of my duty – to help as much as I can,' he said. Perhaps in return, he suggested gently, I might help him? The United Church of Scotland had produced a book, a biography of Chief Onoyon Iya Nya of Akani Obio Eniong. His own copy had been destroyed in the Biafran war, and the Moderator wondered if I might be able to order him a replacement in Britain?

'I am the Chief's son,' he said.

As he spoke, his wife sat on the floor playing with their gurgling grandchildren. On the wall behind him, next to the Annual Pictorial Calendar of the Calabar Presbytery, was pinned one of those cards.

When I asked why, he replied: 'An example to my flock.'

Sister Elizabeth's faith had led her to interpret the executions as a very different kind of lesson. She was heartened to find that her class of teenagers at St Mary's had been appalled. She hoped the news had bolstered their belief that life was sacrosanct.

'Good can come out of evil,' she muttered, like a prayer.

'I am one of the young ones. I came here only recently, 1942,' she began her biography, lowering herself on to a bench at the edge of the playground. 'When our sisters first came there were no schools, so they brought in the young girls to train them for marriage. They did home economics, dressmaking, things they would need in the home to make good wives. Cooking, washing, laundry . . . the custom was that people would come to the convent to pick out their wives, and they would marry straight from the convent.

'I first taught in the north, in Kaduna. I taught the girls home economics – how to make beds, polish wooden floors, how to set and sit down at table.' Her blue-veined hands tucked her grey hair back under her white veil.

'The boys learnt Irish jigs and "Danny Boy". We used to give variety concerts,' she giggled.

'Lagos is full of my ex-pupils. I can't walk down the street without somebody shouting at me. I wonder how they recognise me, I must have changed as I get older. "Ah, but you are still the same," they tell me.

'I've taught mothers and their daughters. The mothers keep telling me, "Ah sister, you don't get them to do things that you got us to do at all. Why don't you get them to polish the dining-room table as we used to do?"'

We wove the hot afternoon around the pictures in her photograph album. Under a sketch of a black child being taught by white nuns was written, 'Moses taken from the wilderness – but not on the Nile.' A gaggle of sisters under white umbrellas lay on a mattress in the back of a mammy wagon. 'Annual Holiday, Jos 1953' was written in neat handwriting underneath. Jos was the cool mountain holiday resort for administrative officers during the colonial period.

'When I first came out, it was believed that the sun affected you through your head,' said Sister Elizabeth. 'We all had to wear helmets made of cork on top of our headscarves. Thank goodness that theory didn't last long – the only place you could buy the helmets was Princes Street in Liverpool. The one item of shopping we had to get before boarding was a helmet. But then they decided the sun affected you through your eyes, so we all had to wear dark glasses.'

The *Andalucia Star* had brought Sister Elizabeth, among over three hundred passengers, to Africa. She had worked her way slowly, adjusting to her new life as she made her way southward and eastward. Travelling without a convoy, the ship had zigzagged across the ocean, almost touching America to avoid the U-boats. Bunkering at the Canaries, the young Sister Elizabeth had seen Africans for the first time working in the port. In Freetown, awaiting the small boat that would take her further south, she first set foot on African soil. At Takoradi her cabin trunk of serge dresses was lost and a missionary lent her a tropical habit, before transferring on to another boat to take her on to Lagos. On the return voyage, the *Andalucia Star* was destroyed by a torpedo off the West African coast.

'Nigeria's a place you get attached to,' she said.

'But don't you miss things?'

'The fields in Ireland where I lived are covered in daffodils. I remember once asking my mother why. She said when we were young and a kitten died, we planted the bulbs over the top of the kitten's grave. Sometimes I long for those daffodils.'

The *Minos* wasn't due in to Lagos from Liverpool for another week, so I left the Second Secretary's compound for a foray into Rivers State. I had heard of a town called Bonny, once a great slave-trading and palm-oil centre, only accessible by boat through the Niger Delta. When Bonny was a major trading port looking out to sea, no road was necessary. With the interior inaccessible to strangers, the Bonny traders controlled the flow of raw produce towards the coast and manufactured goods inland, and flourished. Now that same inaccessibility is the cause of the town's decline. With no trade and the only way to reach the town through the creeks, Bonny is a backwater withering away.

I sped to Port Harcourt, capital of Rivers State, by flying coffin. From Bonny Waterside on Creek Road, I took the motor launch through a web of streams. The boat was so laden with heavy madam market traders and their goods that my hand trailed over the side through the brown water until it felt quite numb. The shiny white Shell launch carrying men from Bonny Oil Terminal buzzed past like a fussy fly and disappeared in seconds, leaving a lingering scar in the heavy water.

We passed the giant carcass of a ship, wrecked on its way up-river through the sandbanks and swamps. Nature has constructed the most effective fortifications for the interior. For four centuries, the veins of the Niger Delta had kept European commerce from penetrating any further than a few miles from the coast. One stream looks very much like any other, walled by mangrove swamps which are flooded by the water at high tide. Landmarks are so few that the chart lists 'A conspicuous umbrella-shaped tree' as a point from which to take a bearing. Once entered, a boat could be lost in the maze of creeks for days. The name of the town which nestles over four hundred miles up-river grew to mean the furthest imaginable place – Timbucktu.

The town of Bonny on the east bank at the mouth of the Bonny River had developed into a major palm-oil port during the nineteenth century, from where African entrepreneurs acted as middlemen between the inland markets and the European traders trapped on the coast. The Bonny traders adopted European names: Wilcox and Green being the most popular. There was also a big trader with webbed hands called Captain Hat, who employed a slave to carry his umbrella and take his hat on and off, which was how he is said to have come by his name. And there was the Jumbo family, who were so called because they never forgot how many casks of palm oil they had exchanged. The precious oil changed hands in vast quantities and by the turn of the century there was a telegraph office and a dozen trading hulks belonging to British and German firms permanently moored along Bonny's waterfront. Greens, Wilcoxes, Harts (from Hat) and Dan-Jumbos (Portuguese for 'son of Jumbo') populate Bonny today, and the older men of these once prosperous families still wear the Edwardian collarless shirts with mock frills sewn down the front that symbolised their wealth during the good times.

As the launch swung round to the half-submerged jetty, a string of shacks stretched out higgledy-piggledy along the front. Constructed from large sheets of corrugated iron, Bonny looked like a town made from a pack of playing cards. After much commotion, the other passengers shuffled up the jetty and rattled through one of the metal doorways. I made my way up from the launch and turned into what appeared to be the main street running parallel to the water's edge. There was nobody in sight except a handful of dusty children who heralded my arrival:

> 'Amingo pepper,
> If you eat pepper
> You will yellow more more!'*

I paraded up the main street like the Pied Piper with his procession, being amingo-peppered all the way. Halfway up, opposite a sign reading 'Palm Garden Hotel', was a grand, two-storeyed grey cement block building with wooden shutters and columned verandas, flying the green and white Nigerian national flag from a huge pole. In front, resting on three white pillars and protected from the sun by its own little sloped roof, was an enormous tablet:

Fruit of Labour

Built by Chief E.G. Jene
in Memory of His Late Father Jene Dan-Jumbo
A Man of Singular Dexterity and Patriotic Ambition
Who Found Wealth Through Honest Labour and Fame Through
Wisdom and Kindness
A Hero of the Fubara-Opubo Civil War of 1869,
the Ashanti War of 1875 and the Bonny-Kalabari War of 1880.
He was Equal to None in the Making of 19th Century Bonny
Born 1844 and Died Peacefully 1909

This grand house advertised itself as the home of the most important person in Bonny, so I decided to introduce myself.

The door opened directly on to a surgery, and Dr A. 'Steve' Dan-Jumbo (as a notice on his desk read) was sitting opposite it wearing black-rimmed glasses and white shorts. A dozen dark hairs curled like insects on his fine chest.

'My time is not my own,' he smiled, and pointed to a chair. 'This is a private practice. My patients could need me at any time.'

I took this to be an explanation for his having been unemployed when I entered.

On a shelf behind him stood the picture of medical student Steve Dan-Jumbo and a sharp-nosed English woman in an unimaginative round black hat and severe suit. There was a small group of guests at

---

*Folklore says that white people look so sick because they don't eat enough of the small piquant red peppers used in Nigerian dishes. Eating plenty of them is supposed to darken the skin. In Bonny, 'amingo' is used as a greeting to white people, from the Portuguese for friend.

the register office. A few curled photographs of coffee-coloured children were propped up between books with imposing titles embossed on them in gold lettering – *Gray's Anatomy of Physiology* and *The Human Mind in Its Complexity*.

Dr Dan-Jumbo was glad I had made his humble home my first port of call on arriving in the town of Bonny.

'But I am afraid it would not be possible for you to stay here. My wife is away,' apologised the doctor. The length of her absence was not specified. 'But please be my guest at the Palm Garden.'

I refused in a stuttering English manner, the doctor insisted, and so I relented and accepted his generous offer. He would have taken me across and introduced me to the proprietor, but, he regretted, 'My time is not my own.'

At the door we shook hands.

'I trained at King's College, Cambridge,' the doctor solemnly announced as I took my leave to cross the road.

The Palm Garden Hotel was whirring like a dragonfly from the overhead fans. I was surprised to see a tiny plump white woman sitting in the foyer, either reading or hiding behind a *Woman's Realm* magazine. I rang the bell on top of the reception desk and waited. No one arrived. I was aware that the *Woman's Realm* had been lowered and I was being watched. The woman slapped down her magazine and scampered over.

'I saw you come off the boat,' she rushed out. 'Couldn't *wait* to meet you. I'm Mandy. Mandy Francis. I couldn't *believe* you were stopping here. This is my fourth month.' She took a gasp for breath.

Mandy and her husband rented the Palm Garden Hotel's best room on the first floor at the front. Ted was a contractor at the Shell compound on the end of the peninsula, painting the inside of the crude oil storage tanks. They were from Merthyr Tydfil and had been all over the place painting the inside of things, big industrial things, but, as far as Mandy was concerned, Bonny was the pits.

'The *pits*,' she said. 'Will you be here long? You *must* have supper with us tonight. I've taught the cook how to make Cornish Pasties.'

I had only been in my room a few minutes when there was a scratch at the door.

'It's me-ee,' sang Mandy. 'Come and have a drink in my room. Girls talk!'

Mandy and Ted's room had a balcony, two overhead fans, and an

en suite bathroom in which water ran about three times a week.
There was a photograph of two squirrellish children, miniature
Mandys, next to a cassette recorder whining out pop music.

'Can't *tell* you how excited I was to see you going into the
doctor's. Thought you might be his wife,' she added.

Mandy and Ted were the only guests at the Palm Garden; I was
the first newcomer since a salesman selling sports and leisure wear
had passed through over a month before, hoping to find a market
with the Shell oil workers. Mandy had the run of the hotel as if it
were her own home and the proprietor's family her domestic staff.
She fussed around, supervising the cooking in the kitchen, fanning
out curled copies of old women's magazines on the tables in the
lobby, and ordering that the corners be swept properly.

We sat on the balcony sipping Zit (Nigerian lemonade) and gin
while Mandy told me how miserable she had been for the last four
months and I watched Bonny unwind for the afternoon. Every half
an hour or so the soporific stillness was rippled by a small boy
dragging his feet along the main street. The doctor's flag hung
flaccid on its mighty pole. Occasionally a customer came out
through the swing doors of a nearby bar, took a deep breath of the
dead air, and pushed his way back inside.

'Prostitutes,' sniffed Mandy. 'That's where they all hang out. One
came up here the other day and asked if I wanted to have sex with
her. Ten naira!' she exclaimed, as if appalled by the prices in a local
supermarket. 'Ten naira!'

At the opposite end of the street to the jetty, where the
corrugated iron houses stopped, the tarmac ran in a grey line to the
gates of the Shell compound, a mile out of town. Nigeria now
imports palm oil, and Bonny's only trade is crude black oil drawn
from the rigs a few miles out to sea in the Bight of Biafra and stored
in the tanks painted by Ted. It has enriched Nigeria – ninety-five per
cent of the country's foreign exchange earnings come from this oil –
but not Bonny. A dozen British engineers live in the compound on
short-term contracts. They have a club, bar and cinema, and are
never seen in town.

Shell (Nigeria) Limited laid electricity lines to the compound,
and allowed the electricity board to use them in return for a small
annual charge. NEPA (standing for National Electric Power Authority, but known as Never Expect Power Again) has never paid the

bill, so I was told that the power is turned off every Wednesday to remind the townspeople not to take Shell's generosity for granted.*

There is one other paved road out of town, in the same direction, turning off inland before reaching the compound. In less than a mile, this too runs out. Successive governments have promised a road to Bonny and added a few yards to the patchwork of tar. But the cost of construction over the swamps and streams – estimates say there would be a bridge for every mile – is colossal.

At the edge of town closest to the Shell compound, on the side of the main street closest to the water, is the old Commonwealth Graveyard, the size of a vegetable patch and littered with ornate Victorian graves. James Hart, who had been struck down by blackwater fever in 1899, aged thirty-two. Major General Denzil Hammill, the British Deputy Commissioner and Vice-Consul sta-tioned at Bonny, laid to rest in the graveyard at fifty-one. And,

> In the midst of Life we are in Death
> Sacred to the Memory of
> John Hepton Claxton Williams
> eldest son of
> John Aldersey Williams
> of Liverpool
> Who died at Cromwell Factory
> Bonny River
> of Yellow Fever
> on Sunday 11th July 1891, aged 31
> Beloved and lamented by a large number of friends
> at home and abroad

I found Mary Kingsley's friend Captain Boler buried nearby. She took tea with him in Bonny in August 1893 and cheerily discussed the yellow fever epidemic, which would soon claim him.

*This is what the townspeople of Bonny believed. But Shell write, 'Shell has not, and does not, cut off the supply to NEPA for non-payment of bills. Electrical power to the town is only interrupted when the circuit breakers of NEPA trip when domestic electricity demand exceeds the safe limit of the installed system.' Shell also points to the many benefits that they have brought to Nigeria. This is undoubtedly true. Wooden desks in Bonny's school have DONATED BY SHELL stamped in large letters along one side.

Children clambered all over the remains of John Hepton Claxton Williams and Captain Doubleday Boler as I photographed their graves, amingo-peppering and jostling to get into the picture.

The light had nearly fallen and the mosquitos were rising from the malarial mud of the swamps as I walked back to the Palm Garden. Two men came suddenly from behind, linked their arms in mine, and hurried me up stone steps into a strip-lit room, dropping me into a chair. Another man was waiting for me, sitting with one leg hooked over the edge of a desk and tapping his knee with a plastic card. He held it out for me to read:

Fubara A. Green
Nigerian Security Organisation

The men who had brought me in pulled out chairs and started a game of cards in the corner.

'Passport,' barked the man on the desk.

This was a favourite trick tried by Nigerian officials of all kinds. Policemen, customs officers, even bank clerks demanded to see a passport, found something wrong with your visa, or your vaccination certificate, or the record of your currency transactions, and asked twenty naira for the passport's return. I had learnt not to carry any documentation about with me.

'I don't have it with me.'

'What are you doing in Bonny?' he continued.

'Tourist.'

He let out a long, laughing sigh. 'We have no tourists in Bonny.'

I could only agree with him.

'I have been watching you. I see you take snaps,' he began, with the air of conducting a serious investigation.

'Yes. Of the Commonwealth Graveyard,' I confessed.

'You snap the children.'

'Yes.'

'They have no clothes on.'

'Well – some of them are wearing shorts.'

'You snap the children with no clothes on, take the snaps to your country, and sell them for pornography.'

The word pornography sounded so absurd and complicated in Bonny.

'You are filthy!' and he hit the desk with his identity card. 'Give me your camera.'

I tightened my grip on the strap.

'I must confiscate your film. We want no pornography in Bonny. You can't sell our children.'

The men in the corner continued slapping down their cards, trying to beat each other's hand. It all seemed so ridiculous until the interrogator picked up the ruler and held it against my cheek.

'Your camera, amingo.'

I must have sat in that chair for two hours or more, grasping the camera to my chest. Fubara A. Green cursed and insulted me, accused me of making millions from pictures of semi-naked African children, then gave up and let me, and my camera, go free.

It was Cornish Pasties for supper at the Palm Garden that evening.

'To make you feel at home,' said Mandy, fidgeting with excitement at entertaining her first guest.

I spotted the doctor next morning as I was walking to the edge of town, close to the only other private medical practice in town. The Chronic Disease Clinic was a corrugated iron hut that was mostly a veranda held up by thick wooden poles with a few square feet of covered space at the back. It advertised on a wooden sign outside.

GONORRHOEA – BARRENNESS – IMPOTENCY – ETC.
TRADO – MEDICAL – CHEMICALS.

Doctor Dan-Jumbo was walking very upright past the Chronic Disease Clinic and swinging a stick, the traditional symbol of chieftainship although Dr Dan-Jumbo was not a chief. The doctor and I exchanged pleasantries. He hoped I was enjoying my stay at the Palm Garden and asked that I would come and have tea with him soon. As we parted with great ceremony, he revealed yet more of his impressive curriculum vitae. Due to the 'Nigerianisation' of foreign-owned businesses, the doctor held the very important position of the Chairman of Shell (Nigeria) Limited.*

*The London office of Shell were quick to counter Dr Dan-Jumbo's claims. 'Doctor Steve Dan-Jumbo is not a Shell employee; he is the chairman of a company that supplies marine vessels under contract to, among others, Shell.'

When I had been in Bonny for four days and felt unwell for the last two of them, a visit to Doctor Dan-Jumbo's surgery seemed sensible.

'My time is not my own,' he smiled, plunging a thermometer between my lips. It was Wednesday and dark inside the shuttered surgery. The doctor took the thermometer out into the blistering sun, peered at it through his thick glasses for a few minutes, and looked solemn.

'Hot and cold flushes?' He began to list the symptoms of malarial fever.

'No.'

'Headaches?'

'No.'

'Aching limbs?'

'No,' I replied. 'I've got a sore throat.'

'Ah! That often accompanies it. You have malaria,' he pronounced gravely.

The *Minos* was due in at Apapa within a few days, and I had to make my way back to the capital and collect my trunks from the Second Secretary's compound. When I boarded the launch next morning bound for Port Harcourt, I felt dreadful. I had taken Dr Dan-Jumbo's prescription of two great doses of Avloclor for a malaria I didn't believe I had, and the effects of the chloroquin cure were proving worse than the disease.* Mandy had come to see me off and waved and waved until our first turn took us into the maze of streams and flooded the bottom of the boat with murky water. We whined through Puffing Billy and Boler Creek. Our wake turned slowly over the dead branches of the mangroves writhing up around us like serpents from the heavy mud.

I left these daydreams of Africa behind in my cabin and drifted out on to the deck of the *Minos*. We were passing thirty miles off Bonny on a slight sea. Later in the voyage I looked up the entry for the Bonny River in the *Africa Pilot*, which is compiled from information sent in by sailors to the Hydrographer of the Royal Navy to

*Avloclor is a very safe and effective chloroquin treatment for malaria, or suspected malaria. Malaria kills so quickly, that it is common for doctors to prescribe anti-malarial drugs even if they are uncertain of the diagnosis – a 'better safe than sorry' approach.

guide seafarers through the dangerous waters of the coast. It read: 'The weary monotony of the mangroves in the lower part of the delta has a most depressing effect.' Then continued:

Reports indicate that a number of ships in Bonny River have been boarded and their crews attacked by armed thieves. Masters are advised to take all possible security measures on board; it has been recommended that a jet of water be kept running continuously down hawse pipes to discourage attempts to board through them.

'Medical attention,' the *Pilot* advised – perhaps with the pressures on Dr Dan-Jumbo's time in mind – 'is available only in extreme emergencies.'

The *Minos* was in no hurry to reach Douala, the major port of Cameroon. There were only some sacks of coffee beans and more empty containers awaiting her. We steamed along at twelve knots, well under full speed, meeting the shipping line's directive to cut back on fuel costs. But when a radio message came through to Doug that there was also a small consignment of timber to be collected at Douala, a satisfied hum buzzed around the ship. Timber was loose cargo, and carrying it on deck was like wearing a carnation in your lapel or a silk handkerchief in your top pocket. It was a visible sign that they were engaging in real trade, and made the seamen proud of their ship.

From the 1860s, the shipping line had run a West African service. Once, when the competition for cargo had been fierce, the shipping line had published timetables in the newspapers advertising their service:

The Steam Ship Hope, Commander Captain A. McIntosh, will leave Liverpool on Wednesday the 21st April at 4 a.m., calling at Madeira, Teneriffe, Goree, Sierra Leone, Monrovia, Cape Coast Castle, Accra, Lagos, Bonny, Old Calabar, Camaroons, and Fernando Po. All freight must be prepaid. The destination, in letters two inches in length, must be marked on two sides of every package.

Sometimes the notice provided a sketch of the vessel on which you or your possessions would be sailing.

By the time I joined the *Minos*, there were few competitors to carry what was left of the West African trade. Rubber, timber, palm oil and cocoa butter had been gradually replaced by synthetic products or cheaper and more reliable Far Eastern supplies. Import controls on luxury manufactured goods enforced by West African governments and the tied exchange rates at which European companies were obliged to trade, made an independent West Africa an increasingly unattractive market to her former colonisers. Now the *Minos*'s line was the only British company running the route, and the fleet, once sixty-strong, had been reduced to six ships.

Although our destination was Liverpool, any number of West African calls lay between us and our home port. Any cargo was worth a long diversion, and a radio message could call us in to Lome, Freetown, or Dakar. In Apapa I had written a postcard home to a man I loved in Britain, and handed it to the agent as he left the ship with the final orders. It gave the name of the ship and our estimated date of arrival in Britain. My estimate was to be weeks out.

On the bridge for First watch, Third Mate Billy Kelly was duty officer. I had spotted his dark curly hair over the gulf between the two dining-room tables. He was clean shaven with a thick-set peasant's body – no resemblance whatsoever to the dashing Errol Flynn I had expected to find in charge of the wheelhouse. Nor was his crewman at the helm a souwestered, grey-bearded man with his hands (showing stumps where two fingers should have been), gripped around a cartwheel and eyes creased against the spray. Instead I had entered a carpeted room with a tiny wheel lost among the dials on the central console, at which a black man stood in a boilersuit, one hand resting lightly on a brass-tipped spoke.

The ship's superstructure – the accommodation block surmounted by the bridge – was at the stern. The wheelhouse windows stretched across the width of the bridge, giving an uninterrupted view of the foredeck – past five pairs of giant red samson posts, known as goal posts, which balanced the cargo derricks – to the bow. And beyond that to the ocean.

On the bridge wing outside, a Kru rating stood on lookout, wrapped in a giant waterproof. Cocooned in the comfort of the bridge, I could only hear the chunder of the engines. 'Southwesterly swell, cloudy and clear,' read the Deck Log kept beside the charts, but from the bridge it was a silent sea.

In a soft Irish accent, Billy explained the layout of the bridge, pointed to the radar scanners, traced his thick fingers over the pencilled line on the chart which indicated our course, and offered me a cup of coffee which he made from a kettle kept at the back near the door.

I flicked through the Deck Log. 'Rolling and pitching easily' was a common entry. Another read 'Shipped water', followed by a line of numbers – 6, 11, 12, 24. An index at the front showed that day had been rough – heavy storm, gale force winds, and water on board. At least the Deck Log promised adventures.

Billy explained how we were passing through the eighteen-mile-wide channel between the island of Fernando Po and the coast of Cameroon. The light of Punta Europa, in a tower on the north-west extremity of the island, shone on our starboard quarter. It looked as insubstantial as a passing ship. In the early night, the island capital Malabo became a string of orange lights.

Fernando Po had been thrown up as the largest in a necklace of islands in the Bight of Biafra, leaving a ten-thousand-foot volcano ringed with black sand. The Portuguese named it Ilha Formosa, the Beautiful Isle. In the eighteenth century the Spanish exchanged Ilha Formosa for mainland claims and called it Fernando Po. When Macias Nguema Biyoga came to power at independence in 1968, Fernando Po became the administrative centre for Equatorial Guinea. He renamed it Macias Nguema Biyoga Island. When Biyoga was overthrown by his cousin in a military coup ten years later, the island became Bioko. Everyone still calls it Fernando Po.

I had heard Billy loud and joking over dinner among the junior officers. But when night dropped like a shutter and only the console and the top of the cabinet holding the charts were illuminated, the bridge became an intimate place and Billy bashful. He seemed ill at ease with the brawniness of his own body, as if his slender, sensitive soul had found itself inhabiting the brutal form of a stranger.

'Want to have a go, then?' he whispered.

The steersman set the pilot to automatic and I stood before the wheel for the first time.

'Experiment,' murmured Billy.

I switched off the auto-pilot and twitched the small wheel. The bow dipped and tilted, and showed me the grey of the sea. The tiny amount of human force needed to move this steel hulk was daunting. The dial of the overhead compass flickered.

Most seamen, Billy explained, don't have to look at the compass. They can feel the ship move two degrees under them, see her turn. Each ship has her own individual tendency to swing in certain conditions of wind and sea. A sailor's hands on the spokes soon feel this, and compensate instinctively. To me, the *Minos* was still a cold steel monster to be battled with.

Below, in the galley and engine room, they must have known I had taken over the helm. In his cabin, the Captain must have felt it too, put down *The Army of the Caesars*, and come up to the bridge to test me.

He wiggled on his cap, clasped his hands behind him, and stared out over the bow:

'I travelled among unknown men,
In lands beyond the sea;
Nor, England! did I know till then
What love I bore to thee.

'Who wrote that?' he demanded.

Waiting for confirmation that it was me he was talking to, I didn't reply.

'WHO WROTE THAT?'

'Don't know.'

'Don't know, SIR,' he bellowed. 'Wordsworth. Wordsworth wrote that. Two degrees to starboard.'

'Two degrees to starboard, sir.' My eyes were fixed on the overhead compass.

'Midships.'

I brought the brass-tipped spoke back to the upright, staring through the glass and mimicking the Captain's concentration.

'Midships, sir.'

'Good. Remember that.' And he snatched off his cap and marched from the bridge, leaving me to wonder whether it was the steering or the poetry I mustn't forget.

The Kru steersman relieved me without a word. I glanced at the tape being vomited from a machine recording our course. The needle drew an almost perfect straight line, 092 degrees, then degenerated into a squiggle where I had taken over the wheel.

That night I ventured into the officers' saloon. Half the full complement of officers were there. A vessel the size of the *Minos* would once have been home for up to fifty men, not, as now, a mere two dozen. The cavernous bar was close to empty.

Nobody paid much attention to me, and carried on smoking and chatting and buying each other beers on chits. Jimmy was leaning against the bar, throwing anecdotes over towards the low, lipped tables as if offering raw meat to a ring of lions.

'What's the point in going ashore,' he said, when, in an attempt to join in the conversation, I asked if anyone had been into Lagos. During ten days in Apapa, only the Sierra Leonean crew had ventured in to town. The British officers had remained on board; the only Africa they saw was the part which could smuggle its way past Sissay at the top of the gangway. Wily Africa.

Things had changed in West Africa, and Jimmy remembered when Apapa had been an attractive port for British seamen. An oil-rich Nigeria had boasted nightclubs rivalling Rio, every sailor's favourite port. Fat mammies welcomed you with open arms under the flashing disco lights, holding out long drinks cooled with ice. Now dusty bulbs dangled from the centre of ceilings, flush toilets didn't flush, taps were just decorative adornments to a sink or bathtub. The collapse of oil prices and the plundering of profits by men who were rich without them had destroyed a once prosperous capital. The tower blocks still stood, but how to get to the eleventh floor with no working lift?

I had my own sad tales which I could have told in the bar that night. Nigeria's cultural showpiece is the Benin National Museum in the ancient capital of Bendel State. The museum, a futuristic bungalow, houses the sixteenth-century Benin bronzes. These royal busts and plaques depict palace ceremonies, and were commissioned by the Oba to be displayed on wooden pillars in his court. The Edo sculptors were forbidden, under threat of death, to make castings for any one but him. Their delicacy and realistic style led European art experts to long dispute that they were the work of Africans.

Benin National Museum was built during the good times. Entirely dependent on artificial light, the bronzes now stand in their display cases in dark rooms. Photographs have been taken of all the exhibits for a catalogue which has never been published. On the streets outside, crude replicas are peddled to disappointed visitors.

But Nigerians are a resilient people, and remain proud of their brief period of prosperity and flirtation with Western ways of living.

'Take me to somewhere typically Nigerian,' I had said when Ayo Ekiong, a lecturer in physics at the University of Ibadan, asked where I wanted to go for a night out in town.

We drove along the Oyo Road, slowing to allow the gaunt cattle across the dual carriageway. The body of a man, his yards of white calico clothing unwinding on the road about him, still lay on the central isle where I had driven past him three days earlier on my way from Murtala Muhammed International Airport. Since I had first passed, he had turned over, as someone in his sleep might do, perhaps buffeted by a passing minibus. Before we saw him, we could smell the stench of his bloated death.

We drove past the corrugated-iron-roofed houses, lit by kerosene lamps around which women squatted, podding, peeling, pounding with thickened arms. I saw a naked boy defecate in the ditch at the side of the road, his mother pick off a plantain leaf from the top of a pile she was wrapping round small parcels of pounded yam, wipe him with it, fold the leaf neatly and throw it in the gutter, patting his bottom to send him back to his friends.

Just off the highway and up a short hill stood the Premier Hotel. We entered the chandelier-lit lobby over a worn carpet and walked towards the lift, ascended to the rooftop bar on the eighth floor, admired it (although closed), pressed the lift button again with a 'Ting!', and descended to the lobby.

On our way back to the car, Ayo exclaimed, 'See – Nigeria is a great country. We have fine buildings, just like yours. Now you have seen what the real Nigeria is like.'

I did not tell this story to the men in the bar that night, because I did not trust them. I adored West Africa, and I did not want it ridiculed by a crowd of British officers who seemed to wholeheartedly despise the place. I was not going to provide them with further examples to bolster their prejudices.

'No – not what it used to be,' said Jimmy. 'Glad to be getting out. You'll all see. I'll set myself up a nice little business with the golden handshake.' Then he launched into his stories of West Africa 'when it was a decent place to go ashore'.

The seated officers moaned in agreement and shouted out for more beers.

'No, not like it used to be,' Roger swivelled in my direction. 'Now there's a girl on board.'

I asked Doug for a cigarette. I sensed in him an ally. The Radio Officer was neither bridge nor engine room, a bit of a loner, and my coming on board had made him no longer the shortest member of crew. But it was Jimmy who came to my defence.

'Leave her alone,' he muttered as if he didn't give a damn. 'Just leave her out of it.'

When I went out on deck later that evening, to look at the lights from Fernando Po playing off the water, on another deck, on a tier below, another body looked out. Not towards the land but towards the ocean.

Chapter Three

Base Light Buoy, River Cameroon
LATITUDE 3°53′ NORTH, LONGITUDE 9°31′ EAST

0800 hours. 'We've just dropped anchor. That's what the clatter's about,' explained Doug over a haddock.

'It's not a bad spot to stop,' he said as the fish slithered from the stainless steel pincers on to his plate. I wondered how he chose good spots from bad.

I nodded over to Billy on the junior officers' table, but he dipped his head and went on eating. After we had all exchanged greetings of 'Lovely morning' around the Captain's table, the commanding officer initiated more substantial conversation. Although it is no longer written that officers must not speak before being spoken to, they seemed reluctant to launch upon a fresh topic independent of the thought process of their master. It was up to the Old Man to break the silence around the white tablecloth.

'Lovely place, Australia. You'd like it there,' he turned to me, drawing upon his complete vocabulary of complimentary words in one burst of enthusiasm. 'Mind you, lots of murders. Of hitchhikers and so forth.'

He obviously included me in the 'so forth' category, and ripe for killing. The prospect did not upset him. A dour Aberdonian, he was not an emotional man. I was just another oddity passing through his seaborne kingdom.

Where I came from was a dangerous place. People were being killed all the time. The BBC World Service provided him with the facts and figures. Today it was the football stadium fire, which he reported to his men with plodding persistence and in the grisliest detail. The Captain, with an expressionless face and not even a flicker of a smile, was enjoying himself.

'Five still on the critical list. Bodies so charred they're unrecognisable. Thought they'd found another one but it turned out to be just a melted plastic bag. Bad,' he announced as he prepared for another assault on the bowl in front of him.

Although seafaring is the second most dangerous profession after coalmining, it is not the sea of which sailors are afraid. It is the land. After all, it is the land which collides with a ship and causes her to run aground and sink. Stranding and collision are responsible for over half the Actual Total Losses at sea, far more than any amount of bad weather. Most accidents occur in coastal waters: the English Channel, the North Sea, in the busy waters around Japan, between the islands of the Pentland Firth, in the congested mouth of the Mersey and on the middle-distance trade to the Baltic, Scandinavian and Biscay ports. Here vessels either hit rocks and shallows, are stranded on sandbanks or, attempting to avoid any of these, collide with one another. Even the most confident captain will instruct his second mate, the navigational officer, to chart a course a good distance from the land, especially at turning points. If by any chance the engines fail, the ship is less likely to run aground. Even when the *Minos* was tracing the West African coast from one port to another, we were often too far off to sight land.

The talk around the breakfast table drifted on to the congestion in the port of Douala which meant we could lie at the Base Buoy in River Cameroon awaiting a berth for a day or more. On our port beam, 13,350-foot Mount Cameroon, the highest peak of the Cameroon mountains and the physical boundary between West and Central Africa, sat obscured behind cloud. Until 1922, the mountain had been an active volcano and the Bakweri people who live in its foothills called it Mongo-ma-Loba, the Throne of Thunder.

As we sailed southward and eastward from Apapa to Douala, we had met the rains. The closer to the equator, the earlier the wet season begins, until a belt around the equator itself suffers thundery rains twice a year. In the early morning we had crossed the fourth parallel and the skies became gloomy. It continued to rain ceaselessly through a grey afternoon. We received a go-ahead to weigh anchor and start for Douala at midnight, but the weather might delay the loading of the ship in berth ahead of us.

On the bridge all was quiet. Billy was on duty. The *Minos* swung gently to her anchor. The narrow channel into Douala, dredged from the shallow water supporting the swamps, swayed in and out of the glass screen.

Unlike the landsman, who thinks all sea looks the same, the seaman finds it difficult to identify the shore. From the water, land can look remarkably uniform and misidentification of a landmark is a frequent cause of accidents: ships steer an incorrect course and founder. Along much of the West African coast, the mangroves stretch for hundreds of miles. The only breaks are the broad mouths of the many rivers, but even these are often indistinguishable from the surrounding swamp.

A radio message spluttered into the quiet bridge.

'This is MV *Apollo*. This is MV *Apollo*. Calling British vessel three points on starboard bow, distance two miles.'

Apollo was a Greek ship, and Greek ships are cursed by British sailors. Greeks were always radioing in for information; it is said that a Greek won't buy a chart if an atlas will do. Their ships are run on a tight budget, and as a result they offer competitive rates and are serious rivals to North European shipping lines. But there is a price to pay for cutting costs: Greece loses more ships per year than any other flag, including the Panamanian and Liberian flags of convenience.

The buoys which marked the channel into Douala were unreliable and unlit at night, so navigation had to be done from the chart and by taking bearings from a tower on Cap Cameroon and a pylon on Pointe Suellaba. The *Apollo*'s chart was old; the Greek Mate said he had heard the buoys had moved. Could we give the true positions?

'Standby,' Billy repeated, putting down the receiver and dodging over to look at the chart.

'Standby,' he said again after – having said he was sorry but he couldn't help – the Greek Mate had coaxed him into taking a second look. Our chart was also old; it would be a lot of work to calculate the positions.

'No,' he apologised and shook his head as if the Greek Mate could see him. 'Sorry. Over.'

'Greeks!' he exclaimed, wallowing over to the kettle. 'Greeks! Always cutting corners. Coffee?'

'Sure.'

'I'd like you to tell me about that traveller sometime,' he said with his back to me as he poured water from the kettle.

'Mary Kingsley?'

'Yeah, her. What exactly did she do, if you know what I mean.'

'She wrote a book about her travels, among other things.'

'Have you got a copy?' Billy scraped his feet about on the floor as he spoke, as if half-hoping his words would be lost amongst the shuffling.

'Yes.'

'Could I borrow it?' He was staring at his coffee mug.

'Sure.'

I finished my coffee with Billy and went on deck. Four flags were flying from the ship. On a pole rising from the stern hung the red ensign, damp and limp. From the masthead flew the crown of the company flag. As we were waiting to go in to port, a solid yellow quarantine flag (with the code letter Q – Quebec), meaning 'I have a clean bill of health', had to be flown until the port health officials had checked the ship and that our vaccination certificates were in order. Then there was the bright green, red and yellow flag of our host country, Cameroon. When the pilot came on board to guide us in, a half-red and half-white flag would be hoisted (H – Hotel), meaning 'I have a pilot on board'.

Jimmy saw me scribbling all this down in a Nigerian school exercise book sold under the trademark 'Onward Big Forty Leaves', disappeared into the purser's office, and came out and handed me a handsome red-spined leather notebook from the store to use as a log.

It is required by statute that a Deck Log and an Official Log Book are kept on board a ship. The Deck Log records the handling of cargo, weather and wind conditions, navigational details, watch officers and the performance of the ship. It is stored on the bridge next to the charts, and filled in by the duty officer. The Official Log Book, supplied by the Department of Trade and Industry and to be returned to them at the completion of a voyage, is kept in the captain's cabin, to be written up by the master of the vessel. This log book is the record of life on board during the voyage – ship's business, fire drills, stowaway and contraband checks, pilfering of cargo, illnesses, notes of protest and a record of the seamen's conduct. Written in the Standing Instructions to Officers of the Bridge Order Book is the ruling that no one but the master of a vessel is allowed to keep such a log. Only one version of events is permitted on board – the captain's. 'I'll log it,' is the master's final threat to enforce his authority.

There is a story – maybe true, maybe not – behind the ruling about who may keep a log. In 1909, a young Harley Street surgeon, stricken with a weariness that had many unpleasant symptoms but no single diagnosable cause, prescribed for himself a long sea voyage and signed on as ship's doctor on a cargo vessel. Sailing from Liverpool to the Far East, he recorded all he saw on board and ashore in Port Said, Java, Penang and Macassar. Buried amongst his exotic tales was a gentle portrait of a love affair between a Japanese tea-house girl and the Second Mate.

Returning to Britain, the surgeon wrote up his journal of the voyage in an attempt to exorcise from his troubled mind the memories of his ship and shipmates which seemed to be continually calling to him. Eight publishers rejected his manuscript, before an editor at Chapman and Hall called Arthur Waugh, father of Evelyn and Alec, recognised the doctor's talent and signed him up.

The Surgeon's Log was an immediate bestseller. The surgeon and his publisher were delighted. So was the Second Mate, and he sent a copy of the book to his wife in Liverpool so she could read about his working life. But the Second had read no further than the first three chapters, and his wife was soon suing him for divorce on the grounds of adultery with the Japanese tea-house girl.

The publisher and the surgeon were even more delighted as the scandal pushed *The Surgeon's Log* into reprint after reprint. But the paternalistic shipping line grew concerned. Anxious for their own reputation and that of their seamen, they inserted a ruling in the Standing Instructions to Officers: No one but the master of this vessel may keep a record of ship's business and any related matters.

The Harley Street surgeon next authored *A Text-Book of Venereal Diseases* and *Lectures on Gonorrhoea*, then turned to writing fiction.

Jimmy's gift of a log was a quiet act of rebellion, as if he had charged me with recording an alternative perspective on life on board. 'Off Douala' I wrote at the top of the page in my new log. But my first entry was a record of the land:

I am sitting on deck and looking out at Mount Cameroon. It is a massive, huge, grey solid rock only two shades darker than the surrounding sky. Mongo-Ma-Loba they call it. The Throne of Thunder.

The sun is setting to one side and cutting a small slither of orange into the grey of sea and sky. Mongo looks like a breast of a woman lying on her back bathing in the sea. There's a small rounded roused bump at the summit. A young woman at rest. Africa the woman.

Her nipple is smudged with a cloud. The swampy land at the foot traces a thick black line along the edge of the creek. Smoke rises cloudlike at irregular intervals along this line. But the village that it rises from is no longer visible. On the side of the mountain, one light twinkles.

The same day the Captain called me in to his cabin and gave me a very different gift – a short history of the *Minos* which he had typed up himself. It was half a page long.

The *Minos* was the third ship so-called. *Minos* (I) had been destroyed by fire after a violent explosion on board in 1953, and scuttled as a total loss. But seamen aren't sentimental about names, and there is no ill-luck attached to them, even if a ship meets a tragic end. So *Minos* (II) was launched, with accommodation for twelve passengers. She had ended her days in a Taiwanese scrap yard.

MV *Minos* (III) had been built in Nagasaki nine years ago, and sold to the shipping line who had registered her under the British flag. When West African trade was slack, she was chartered out and given a name associated with the line for whom she was sailing; the *Minos* had sailed under seven names. Under a different company ensign, the British officers and Kru ratings had taken her to Brazil or the Far East, far away from West Africa. Once, in an effort to cut costs, she had been moved to the Panamanian flag of convenience, but within eighteen months she was again flying the red duster.

I slipped the *Minos*'s half-page history into my log and went to the officers' saloon. Jimmy was off the wagon, he announced on entering the bar. The atmosphere in the bar seemed to depend entirely upon whether Jimmy was 'On the wagon' or 'Off the wagon', so he announced which he was immediately, to let the drinkers know what kind of evening lay ahead. Off the wagon, Jimmy indulged the officers in stories of his time at sea. Jimmy's tales were so infectious and appealing that soon all the other officers would be joining in, recalling when Kruboys washed the wooden decks and deck passengers slept among the ropes at the stern with sheets of canvas stretched over them to protect them from the rains.

'No, it's not like it used to be,' said Billy with nostalgia. 'It used to be special. Film night used to be a real occasion. We had an old projector and put up a screen in the bar. It was like being at the movies, made it different from other nights. We used to get some crap films and that, but it was good.'

I glanced at the blank TV screen. Videos were stacked haphazardly underneath. *Mad Max II, Guns of Navarone, Confessions of a Window Cleaner, Lust* . . . Billy caught me trying to read the title and drew my attention away, claiming to recall the canvas swimming pool, strung up with rope through giant eyelets, which took the skin of your nose off when you dived into it. It was a pool in which Billy, who had only been an ocean-going sailor for three years, could never have swum.

Next, Jimmy elaborated on wild and imaginative plans for his bright future after his voluntary redundancy was accepted. These varied day by day and included opening a pub restaurant with a retired chief mate, but the most common was a market stall selling Marks & Spencer seconds.

On the wagon, Jimmy was miserably sober, complained about his Chief Cook George Kamara like a husband would a recalcitrant wife, remembered an early and long gone marriage to a West Indian woman, and mourned the loss of his West Africa. The bar was gloomy when Jimmy was on the wagon, but there was nowhere else to go.

I sat amongst the men, occasionally trying to join in the conversation, accepting beer after beer as the cans were handed to me from the bar. Billy had sat as far away from me as possible, and never looked over in my direction. He had started to suffer from being allocated as my instructor on the bridge.

'Getting on well with the lady on board?' Roger had ribbed him in the bar. Billy didn't know how to answer back, so thought it was safest to keep away from me.

As I left the bar, awash with Special Strength Skol, and negotiated the stairs up to my deck, Jimmy appeared round a corner and hurried me along to the purser's office where he filled my arms with boxes of Palm Kernel Bathing Lotion, Avocado Shower Gel and Herbal Mango Toothpaste.

'Cargo,' he said conspiratorially. 'Take them out of their boxes in case you meet anyone.'

Accidentally ascending one too many decks on the carefully negotiated course from the purser's office to my cabin, I reached the door marked BRIDGE, through which the solid body of the Captain emerged.

'Lovely evening.'

'Lovely, sir.' I stared at him fiercely, straight in the eye, in an attempt to lock his gaze above my armload of purloined goods.

'Goodnight.'

'Goodnight, sir,' and I waited until he was safely in his cabin before venturing down to my own.

The toothpaste tasted terrible and needed several gargles to remove its foul lining from my mouth.

During the night the Captain's face appeared furiously red and very close to mine, shouting 'I'll log it! I'll log it!' I awoke with furry teeth and in a state of great anxiety, sweating profusely. But then I realised it must have been a dream, because the Captain would never have used the first-person pronoun.

I felt rather cocky as I rinsed off the Avocado Shower Gel and got dressed for breakfast. I had duped the Old Man and been taken into Jimmy's confidence. It was a good beginning. If I could make the rest of the officers accept me, this voyage would be plain sailing.

Chapter Four

Ro Ro Terminal, Douala

LATITUDE 4°03′ NORTH, LONGITUDE 9°42′ EAST

Jimmy changed some money into CFA francs and gave me an old tin army water bottle in a khaki canvas holder as if kitting me out for an expedition. It was May Day, and the port was closed. Shore-workers could not be hired until tomorrow, which meant we would be in dock for at least another twenty-four hours and I had time to venture into the interior. I would make for the light at the foot of Mount Cameroon which I had seen from the deck. It came from a town called Buea, from where Mary Kingsley had begun her ascent of the mountain, the first attempt by a white person on the south-east face.

After breakfast I waited on deck for the gangway to be lowered. Doug was leaning over the rail, sucking on an early-morning cigarette. Already the hawkers, undeterred by the fact that it was a public holiday, were trickling into the dock.

'Hey! Sparky!' a man in a pill-box hat cried up to Doug.

'How's he know I'm the Sparks?' said Doug, looking at me for an answer. 'How's he know?'

'Hey!' he shouted down at the hawker. 'How d'you know I'm the Sparks?'

'Sparky! Sparky! You have shoes?' The man in the pill-box hat pointed energetically at his feet, shod in a pair of leather flip flops. 'Good price. I give you very good price for shoes.'

'He wants to buy my shoes,' said Doug, uninterested. Then, with real wonder, 'But how does he know that I'm the Sparks?'

I ran ashore as soon as the gangway was lowered, eager for the heavy rank smell of Africa. Douala's May Day Workers' Festival had been ousted from the Reunification Stadium by a football

match, so crowds wearing specially printed T-shirts milled around
the town and jumped in and out of taxis. A woman with the slogan
'I'm Proud to Be a Farmer' stretched across her breasts shouted
greetings across the street to a man with 'CAMEROON AIRLINES.
MAY 1st' pulled over his chest.

A young man spotted me hesitantly wandering across the road
trying to hail a taxi, approached and questioned politely – 'Are you
anglophone?' – as if asking my nationality.

'My name is Victor,' he said.

Victor ran along the centre of the road after taxis for me, like a
dog chasing cars, until one stopped and tooted its horn.

'Motopark,' I ordered, waving to a shrinking Victor out of the
back window. From the bus station I would be able to take a bus or
shared taxi to Buea.

In the front, the driver chatted to a woman whom I presumed to
be his wife, who was smothered by two young children. She
bundled herself and her children out of the taxi by a roadside
market and cried farewells. As we started for the motopark, the
driver turned and flashed a smile: 'You like me?'

At the motopark I had to show my passport to buy a ticket for
Buea. A giant poster of the President of Cameroon, wearing a hard
hat and standing in a field of pineapples, looked down on the queue.
'Paul Biya. A Good Example,' was printed underneath in huge
letters. The clerk in the corrugated iron shed, protected by an iron
grill, laboriously recorded all the passengers in a large ledger book.
He took my passport and turned it over and over, then, satisfied that
he now understood this new sort of identity card, took down my
essential details. Under a column headed 'Name' he wrote 'DEA',
and under the column headed 'Carte d'identité' he took down the
number of an old Chinese visa. Then he wrote the licence-plate
number of the vehicle I must board on my ticket.

I presumed this was another Nigerian-style trick to gain dash,
went up to the driver of the first minibus, asked if he was going to
Buea, and took out a thousand franc note. He asked to see my ticket
and shook his head.

I repeated the offer to four more drivers. One insulted me in some
language which I didn't understand but which the passengers
waiting for their buses did, and they joined in the fray, laughing
and slapping themselves at this unexpected theatre. A heavy

madam who had been behind me in the queue at the iron grill was one of the principal players. An hour and a half later I boarded the minibus whose registration plate corresponded with the number on my ticket.*

The heavy madam had the same number on her ticket, and spread her broad body over the back seat intended to hold three passengers. The driver demanded she paid extra: additional fuel would be needed, he argued, to carry her weight. But the woman stubbornly ignored the driver's increasingly furious shouting and flapping arms, bought a boiled egg from a boy hawker with a sticker on his tray reading 'No Credit Thank You Allah', and put the whole egg in her mouth, spitting out splinters of the shell as she ate.

Encouraged by this new principle of payment for taxi fares, a bird-sized man in a shiny nylon suit asked for a discount. It was another hour before we left the motopark for the foothills of the Throne of Thunder.

The thirty-mile drive to Buea, three thousand feet up the side of the mountain, took us through abandoned rubber plantations where row upon row of thin trees arched away from the coast, their silver trunks bent over by the wind from the sea. Down through the lush valley, I caught a view of the water before it disappeared behind more tight rows of silver trunks. The minibus vibrated and the gears grated as we struggled up the road, past a large hand-written sign outside a bush bar boasting 'KOMMEN HEIREIN UND DEUTSCH SPRECHEN MIT PAPA.' Cameroon had been a German colony until the end of the First World War, when the League of Nations had placed the west under British mandate and the east under the French.

Even with the wind blowing through the open side of the bus, it was stiflingly hot. A tear of sweat tickled down my leg like a spider. One by one, the passengers began to disembark, women lowered their children and baskets to the muddy edge of the road, tied children to their backs with a piece of cloth, wound another piece of waxprint in a coil around their heads on which to balance their

---

*All passengers on Cameroonian public transport are personally insured, I later learnt. My personal details and the number plate of the vehicle recorded in the ledger would be proof of my journey, and with this I could be compensated in the event of an accident. That was why it was so important to travel in the correct minibus. Accidents are not infrequent.

loads, and entered the rainy season undergrowth. The moist green vegetation soon absorbed them.

I intended to stay on the bus until it reached the terminus in Buea, but the driver turned and asked me where I wanted to be dropped in town, so I gave him a name we had just passed on a sign at the roadside: 'Mountain Hotel.'

'Alors ici.' The bus came to a screeching halt and he dropped me right there.

Down in the docks it had been squally and overcast, but up in the mountains a crisp breeze was blowing. Buea still had the aura of the mountain resort to which the European penpushers and administrators had escaped from their duties on the coast and breathed in the clear, cool air of the foothills. The roadside was dotted with dainty flowers with yellow centres and daisy-shaped petals like those found in English gardens, not the fetid, succulent, phallic horns of tropical Africa. The sun hung in a perfect yellow sharp-edged orb in a blue sky, then was hidden entirely behind a thick cloud, then came out again as clear as an apple. All the humid haziness of the coast had vanished, and everything stood out sharply in the mountain air.

A bulbous black cloud sat obstinately in front of the mountain summit. Taking the road in the direction it sloped upwards, I came to a sign nailed on a wooden post – 'To Prison and Mountain' – instructing me to turn off on to a sodden path.

I hadn't gone far before a child with the wrinkled face of an adult dodged out in front of me, panting. He wore a nylon turquoise shirt torn from the hem upwards at such regular intervals that it seemed like a deliberate pattern, and bell-bottoms that flapped around his legs. The metal wristband of his watch hung loose like a bracelet on his arm. Peter, he announced, was my guide. He was twelve, he told me, though very small for twelve.

His prospective employer was thoroughly interviewed. Where did I live? How long was I staying? What was I doing? Was I alone?

I answered with a caution bred in West Africa. What, I wondered, did he *really* want to know? West Africa had made me suspicious of a twelve-year-old child.

'Are there many black people in Britain?' he continued.

I said yes, but mostly from the Caribbean, not Africa.

He repeated, slowly, 'Car-ri-be-an', as if to remember it.

He knew, he said, about white people. He knew how they had lots of money, how everything was cheap to buy in their land, how they sometimes take black men back with them.

'Why?' I asked.

'To wash pant,' he said simply. 'They take dem and they wash white man's pant.'

White men's landmarks were pointed out. 'This is where white man park car,' indicating a square of mud cleared from the undergrowth. 'This is where white man drink beer after going up mountain,' pointing at a windowless corrugated iron hut with a padlock on the door.

White men had been coming to Buea for centuries. Before the Germans, the Portuguese had traded slaves for trinkets and named the Wouri River Rio dos Camaroes after the large pink prawns found there, giving the country its present name. When the Germans had raised their flag over Buea in 1885 and made it the capital of their Protectorate, they set about building houses with spindly white towers among the foothills to remind them of home. A dozen German bodies are still resident in Buea, buried in the derelict graveyard behind the petrol station on the road back out of town.

The grandest of the old white colonial buildings, built by third Governor Puttkamer in the style of a mansion on the Rhine and known as the Schloss, is now used by President Biya as his holiday home. From the side of the mountain, its turrets stood out high above the trees. Peter advised me not to take a picture. But from the side of the mountain, I protested, who could see me?

'Only black man can take snap,' he said stiffly.

'Why?'

Peter did not seem to be aware of the origin of the Schloss's design: 'Because white man can take snap and go to his own country and build a house exactly like this one,' he answered.

Peter had devised a method of compensation.

'You must pay,' he said, 'to take a snap of houses here.'

'Who must I pay?'

'The owners.'

'But who does the house belong to?'

'The children.'

'How can it belong to the children?' I asked, feeling at last I had caught him out.

Peter inflated his diminutive adult's body. 'We are Cameroonians.'

Peter was continually twitching his head from side to side.

'Thieves,' he said, when I asked what he was looking for.

'Who are your people?' I asked, meaning to discover whether he was Bakweri or belonged to some other tribe.

'Anglophone,' he answered.

He took me to where we could see 'The Pipe', and explained how it gathered water at the top of the mountain and supplied all Buea. I gave him a black biro, a pair of socks and some loose change. He wanted to know how much the pen cost and where it came from. I said the first thing that came to my mind – 'One dollar' and 'New York'.

I asked where his watch came from.

'My brother,' he said. Another easy answer like mine.

Looking down, I could see for ten miles over broad creeks wriggling through flat green swamps to the town of Limbe, Buea's seaport. The coastline curved and deceived, never letting you know which patch of swamp was mainland and which was an island. The West Coast of Africa is like that. The water blends into and curves around the land until you cannot distinguish which is which.

Looking up, I saw the bulbous black cloud. It moved away from the mountain top in the early morning and at six o'clock each evening, Peter assured me. I snapped the cloud. A boy in a distant house on the side of the mountain thought I was pointing my camera at him, threw himself from his veranda and hurtled towards us down the path like an animated rag doll. He stopped fifty or so yards up the path and glowered at us suspiciously.

We turned away and walked briskly back down the mountainside to the beat of Peter's panting. I entrusted my safety entirely to my tiny guide.

I went to the Mountain Hotel, which had no view of the mountain. There was a lawned and landscaped area at the back with wooden benches and tables, much like an English pub garden, crowded with city workers who had come out to the mountains for the May Day holiday. Amongst the Mountain Hotel's largely European clientele, I hoped sitting alone and writing up my log would at least be politely tolerated.

West Africa allowed little time for introspection. On the mountainside, I had wanted to rest for a few minutes and admire the view,
but Peter had insisted that we press on.

'I want a drink of water,' I would say as an excuse to sit down,
taking out Jimmy's cumbersome flask.

But Peter had continued to chatter away, ferreting around inside
my bag.

'What that colour you have in there?' he asked, pulling out my
pens. 'What that?'

The quiet solitude that a European seeks is treated as a sickness or a
psychological disorder in Africa. When I had stayed in Nigerian
homes, I would sometimes retreat to a corner just to remember who I
was amongst all the strangeness. Soon someone would whisper,
'Seester, how now?' and call me back into the centre of the room,
place me in the best chair, and offer me a mineral. I recalled a
conversation in the apartment at 1004. A group of young women had
been talking about their college days at Calabar University. One
student, they used to laugh about. Aaayee, she was funny. She
bleached her skin – that's why she was so blotchy. She dyed her hair
that funny orange colour. But this woman was stranger than most,
for it was said that she had turned down an invitation with, 'I need to
be alone tonight.' They laughed and laughed, and I laughed along
with them, frightened of being laughed at myself.

I noted this thought down in my log, then left the Mountain Hotel.
Peter was crouching on the steps outside. We had not visited the
water fountain, he informed me with great importance.

The fountain no longer spouted water but the head of the Kaiser
was imprinted on it in an enormous medallion. The children, Peter
explained, cut the grass around the fountain so white man can take
snaps and pay them.

I snapped and paid him. Then I snapped the bright red English
pillar box next to the fountain. The black cloud grew larger and
lower, and threatened rain.

I walked to the edge of town, passed the petrol station and the dead
Germans, and began to hitch. A fat French woman with bloated legs
and greasy grey hair plastered in a thin layer over a large round pink
head picked me up and chattered away to her albino friend in the
front. I struggled with her husband in the back, who worked on the
'chemin de fer' and had been in Cameroon 'neuf ans'.

'À la porte,' I announced when they asked where I wanted to be let off in town, which set the fat wife and her friend into another furious conversation and left her husband stunned.

'La porte? Vous n'intendez pas la poste?' he asked timidly.

In Douala the water sellers had taken shelter from the rain. They crowded under the market awnings, selling Fanta cans filled with water from plastic bottles labelled *Eau de Minerale*. West African states are still flavoured by the tastes of their former colonial masters. Women scurried along the street with baguettes balanced on their heads. Gauloise and Gitane were for sale by the stick at corner kiosks. A gang of schoolboys ran past dressed in long knickerbockers with satchels bouncing on their backs, perfect little black Europeans jabbering in French. In a café, I sat next to a woman who had an enormous photograph of Paul Biya's head printed all over her wrapper, his benign smile blaring out from her thighs and sniggering around the corner of her splendid bottom.

I passed boulangeries displaying croissants, brioches and pain au chocolat. (In Nigeria the only bread available was white and soft, and kneaded into a ball of gum when chewed.) Delicatessens sold selections of fine cheeses and wines. (In Nigeria there had only been Star beer.) The most common type of store, however, was the shoe shop. They were everywhere, several in each street, with smart glass fronts and proper doorways with bells that tinged when a customer entered. I wondered why the man on the quay had been after the Radio Officer's shoes, as footwear seemed to be in abundance in Douala. Then I looked at the styles more closely and realised that they were made not of leather, but rubber.

There were all sorts of luxuries piled up on the market stalls, so I bought myself a small glass bottle of Wet 'n' Wild Vernis A Ongles, a vivid nail varnish, to paint my toe-nails scarlet like a high-class Nigerian woman.

I returned to the *Minos* in time for dinner, flushed with Africa. I painted my nails with Wet 'n' Wild and went to mess. Douala was mistyped 'Doualala' next to the anchor at the top of the menu that evening.

'Want to come to the Club?' asked Fourth Engineer Steve after dinner. 'With Billy, Keith and me?' Keith was the Second Mate, a brash young red-headed Liverpudlian who continually knocked those who called the south of England their home. 'Bloody Londoners,' he called them, whether they came from Cornwall or Hertfordshire. As far as Keith was concerned, anything further away than the Wirral was foreign, and to be mistrusted.

The Club was the Mission to Seamen, intended as a haven for distressed sailors and a provider of spiritual comfort. But the seamen used the missions as bars which sold European beers, and always called them the Mish or the Club.

Douala's Club was in the Foyer du Marin on the road that curved up from the port into the town centre, and was run by a German missionary couple. With Dutch courage from their German beer, we hit the town.

'Dou-a-la-la! Here we are!' cheered Keith as we descended the stairs into the street.

Philip adopted us before we had gone more than a hesitant few yards.

'Philippe. Phillip. Philip,' he beamed. 'Français? Deutsch? Eenglish?'

'Bloody English,' said Keith, affronted by the intimacy of adjectives.

'I know a good place. You'll like it. Music too much. Beer too much. Dancing too much,' and Philip wiggled his hips and gave a couple of claps in anticipation.

'Girlfriend?' he said to me. I thrust my hands deeper into my trouser pockets.

'No. Sailor,' I said.

Steve shot me a quick wink.

Philip whistled through his teeth and slapped me on the back.

'Sailor seester. Come,' and he led us through a town which seemed to play host to a permanent party.

From cassette players swung at the end of baggy waxprint sleeves, through glassless windows, from basements and second-floor apartments, a heavy beat bounced along every street. Small crowds emerged from a doorway, threw back their heads in a loud laugh, scratched the backs of their necks furiously, sighed, then disappeared into another doorway. We marched along the centre of the road, myself and Philip the vanguard; Steve, Keith and Billy behind, shoulders hunched and hands thrust deep and defensively into their pockets.

All such journeys ought to end in a slight deviation from the well-lit main route into a hidden alleyway which, without our trusty guide, would never have been found. Philip did not disappoint. Plunging into a darkened side-street, we made our way lemming-like to the lightbulb at the end which protruded over a closed door. It opened at Philip's push.

Inside the lights were bright and the beat strong. It began as a slow, dull thud, gradually building up into a shorter, sharper rhythm taking the dancer along with it like passengers on a train unable to stop shaking as they speed faster and faster along the line. The room was a noisy mass of wrappers, headties and squirming bodies. The smell of perspiring flesh was intoxicating.

In the middle of all the black bodies Steve wound himself up like a top. His long white limbs dislodged the steady beat of the dancers about him, who instinctively moved away, leaving the Fourth Engineer pirouetting in the only clear space on the dance floor.

In Liverpool, Steve must have been considered handsome. His pale freckled skin, soft strawberry blond hair and grey eyes had a translucent sheen which somehow implied innocence, like an angel. He was a good dancer, moving well and uninhibitedly on the dance floor. In Liverpool, Steve would have been considered a catch.

'Good, good,' Philip chuckled, joining us on the floor and nodding his head towards Steve. Egged on by Philip's comments, I started to move more frenetically. Philip broadened his smile. He interpreted my increased action as flirting.

Perhaps it was. Perhaps I was flirting with Africa. Africa was, after all, what I had come ashore to see, and the more intimate the contact the more satisfying my experience.

Keith and Billy, leaning against the bar, nodded towards us every now and then, and scanned the dance floor. They look ridiculous, I thought, standing there so determined to remain unmoved while everybody bobs about them. What were they looking for?

It was 0130 hours when we left the dance place.

'Early,' said Keith looking at his gold wristwatch. We walked back to the port in silence, paying off Philip at the gate.

'Come again, sailor seester. Come again,' he waved.

'Bloody pimp,' the officers muttered.

But Philip had not obliged them in this respect.

By the time I was up and dressed, the day's work had already begun. Three gangs had been set to work discharging cargo from the hatches and I could hear the Mate shouting at them along the deck.

When I went in for breakfast the two tables in the officers' mess were stripped to their white linen cloths. Through in the galley, the clatter of cutlery being cleaned continued like an African band. I poked my head through the sliding steel door. Jimmy was rinsing his hands and humming. He combined the position of catering officer with medical orderly, and had been visiting a sick sailor.

'What's he got?' I asked.

'He's got gonorrhoea,' said Jimmy beaming. He would have to record the fact in the Catering Officer's Medical Log.

'How d'you know?' I asked.

'I've just been squeezing him,' he said, taking the tomatoes from the fridge for luncheon.

My esteem in the eyes of the seamen increased considerably when I bought the earrings. One of Jimmy's old trading friends came on board, a small charcoal black man wearing an embroidered cap and carrying little leather pouches full of ivory jewellery which he laid on Jimmy's desk.

Alhaji Mohammed Said was a Muslim from Northern Cameroon and well known to the ships' pursers with whom he conducted his business. The First Mate had bought a carved tusk from Mr Said on an earlier voyage in exchange for an old cassette recorder and ten US dollars. The tusk had been carved in a concrete block hut in the centre of Douala where Mr Said employed four men.

Doug had come to my cabin. 'There's some jewellery for sale and you ought to be interested,' he said. It was more a summons than an invitation so I followed him to the purser's office.

Mr Said emptied one of his drawstring pouches gently on to the desk.

'Beau-ti-ful. Beau-ti-ful,' he made a grand show of admiring his own wares, cupping each item softly in his hand and holding it towards his mouth as if to kiss it.

'All real elephant. For the ladies. For the beau-ti-ful ladies.'

I could see Mr Said and I were going to have fun together.

'Bone,' I tutted, walking towards the door. 'They're not elephant at all. They're hippopotamus. Hippopotamus bone.'

'Madam. Madam,' Mr Said called after me, sweeping his arm over the display on Jimmy's desk.

There were wire-thin bangles carved in the pattern of a rope and heavily polished armbands several inches wide. There were earrings shaped like tear drops, or small round beads, or huge flat triangles cut across the tusk to show the pattern of the grain. I picked up a pair of long smooth oval earrings which hung from small gold hooks.

'How much?'

'Six thousand francs.'

'Not bad,' said Doug.

Jimmy coughed at him to shut up.

'In dollars,' I said.

'Twenty dollars,' said Mr Said.

'You're a thief,' and I walked to the door.

Mr Said turned to Jimmy, begging him to vouch for his good character. 'Masar, tell madam that Mohammed Said always gives you a good price. The best.'

'He's a scoundrel,' said Jimmy. 'Offer him ten.'

'Seven dollars,' I said.

'Ten,' said Said.

I turned the earrings over in my hand. They were quite beautiful. The ivory was slightly warm to touch.

'Eight dollars. That's my final offer. Look – they're not even well-made,' and I threw them down amongst the pile on the desk.

Twenty minutes later, after I had learnt of the enormous size of Mr Said's extended family, his three rapacious wives, and his seven children, we agreed on nine dollars.

'You robbed him,' said Doug as Alhaji Mohammed Said and his pouches disappeared down the gangway. By the end of the day I'd been congratulated by everyone except Roger.

'Heard you're not a bad bargainer,' said the Second Mate when I visited the bridge to look at the charts.

By midday the logs had arrived and loading had begun. Jimmy spotted a Swedish vessel coming into port that afternoon whose catering officer he claimed was an old friend, so together with Doug we set out for an evening call. The only time Jimmy and Doug went ashore was to visit another ship. Decked out in their tropical uniforms, the stocky Radio Officer and the mighty Chief Steward strode across the quay towards the *Bothnia Princess*, proud ambassadors of British seamanship.

In the heyday of the West African trade, several ships of one line could be found in any West African port and the seamen would pay each other visits, the officers joining the officers' saloon, the crew the crew's saloon on the deck below. A ship could spend over a week in port as cargo was loaded. Former shipmates would renew their friendship, anecdotes about the Old Man and the purser would be bandied between them, and information about the weather and conditions in the next port of call exchanged. It didn't matter where in the world these old friends met, they passed the evening talking in the officers' bar as if they had met for a jar in their local pub.

In the 1950s, a typical voyage might last two hundred days with over half of these spent alongside. Now twenty-four hours in port is considered a long docking, and shipping companies demand ever faster turnaround times. Visiting another ship was rare, and Jimmy was pleased to be able to show that he still knew 'some of the old lads'.

The *Bothnia Princess* was an altogether different lady to our vessel. She was a roll-on roll-off carrier, with a huge square transom at the stern and a blunted bow. There were no curves anywhere in her design, and she looked more like a floating metal barn than a sea-going vessel.

The Scandinavians have overtaken the British in what is left of the West African trade. Their more technically advanced self-loading vessels, with an all-Swedish crew who are prepared to discharge cargo themselves, cut costs and makes scheduling more reliable. The strict hierarchy of the *Minos* was not observed on these North European vessels. In Scandinavian ships there are no officer cadets. Every seaman starts as an ordinary sailor.

When we reached the *Bothnia Princess*, cars were being driven out from her stern by huge blond seamen and forklift trucks chundered up and down the ramp with containers balanced on their prongs. Jimmy shouted 'Galley?' to a Viking in jeans and T-shirt, who responded by pointing to a companionway.

'No uniforms,' stated Jimmy. 'No pride.'

We ascended up through the decks. Every time Jimmy caught the eye of a blond seaman he'd shout 'Galley?' and they would point their finger towards the sky. Nobody paid us the slightest bit of attention.

'No bleeding security either!' said Jimmy.

When we reached the A deck another blond seaman was waiting with an arm taut as a rope held out to be shaken.

'Ah. You are here!' he greeted. 'The big man and the little man in white uniforms! And the girl! I am Anders, the Purser. How do you do.'

'I'm Patterson. Jimmy Patterson,' said Jimmy. 'This is Doug, our radio officer. And this is Dea. She's sailing with us. Is Lars on board?'

'Lars who?'

'You know. Big bloke.' Jimmy hit his forehead with the side of his palm to indicate height and flexed his biceps to indicate width. 'Blond hair. Clean shaven,' he said wiping down his own grey strands and stroking his chin.

We had passed a dozen men who answered to Jimmy's description in our ascent to the galley.

'I do not know him,' said Anders. 'Can I invite you a Pripps?'

The bar was empty. Compact and tastefully decorated in oatmeal hessian with padded benches lining the walls and low oval pine tables, it bore no resemblance to our ship's orange saloon.

Jimmy was off the wagon.

'Två öl tack,' he let slither out casually.

'Where'd you learn that?' said Doug impressed.

'Worked for a Swedish line for a few months once,' said Jimmy nonchalantly.

'I am Norwegian,' said Anders, going behind the bar.

'Ditt djävla föbannade svin,' said Jimmy, grinning.

'I do not think that is very funny,' said Anders, handing us our Pripps.

'What did you say?' asked Doug eagerly.

'I said "You bloody swine",' said Jimmy, still grinning. 'That and "Two beers please" is the only Swedish I know.

'Just a joke, just a joke.' He turned to Anders, 'Are you sure you don't know Lars?'

Chapter Five

At Sea

LATITUDE 4°03′ NORTH, LONGITUDE 9°42′ EAST TO
LATITUDE 5°37′ NORTH, LONGITUDE 0°01′ EAST

The gangs worked late into the night, loading sacks of coffee and helping themselves to the contents of our containers. At midnight, twelve containers were found to be broken into. 'Excessive pilfering of Cargo at No 3 Hatch' recorded the Mate in the Deck Log. The Captain meticulously wrote down the numbers of the damaged seals in the Official Log in his cabin. We were preparing for sea.

Half an hour before casting off, in accordance with the instructions in the Bridge Order Book, a stowaway search was made. In Nigeria, the recently issued Illegal Aliens Decree had set a deadline by which all unregistered immigrants had to leave the country. When I had joined the *Minos* in Apapa, it had been four days away. At night, the gangway had been wound up and all ropes securely fastened, so no Ghanaian or Cameroonian illegal worker could find a free passage home.

Once a stowaway was on board, the shipowner was legally responsible for him, as if the ship were a country and he had found residence there. So before the ropes were let loose, the hatches, tween decks, and even the crow's nest were thoroughly searched by three officers.

But stowaways have become ingenious, and have been found in the most extraordinary places, including hidden in grain cargo, using small pipes to breathe through. Others destroy their travel documents, often eating them, so their home country cannot be identified. Some travel round the world for years at a time on their adopted ships, and a vessel sometimes has to be sold with a stowaway as a sitting tenant. In the case of the *Johnny Two*, a stowaway refused to speak for five months; he turned out to be a West German with a history of mental problems.

Captains are issued with instructions on how to determine a stowaway's true nationality – ask the colour of the buses or the taxis in the place he claims to be his home town, or the name of the main railway station. One ship's captain put this interrogation technique into practice on a stowaway who had been on board for several weeks and claimed to be a Jamaican citizen:

> He said he lived in Kingston and provided a name of a street which looked as if it could be true. When we interviewed him, our first question was whether he could name any Jamaican cricket players. When he shook his head, we knew immediately that he was certainly not Jamaican.

Even our Captain, a stickler for searches, remembered when 'four little fuzziwuzzies' from Addis Ababa were found on the *Minos*, just off the Egyptian coast, hiding between two hatches.

'Tried to get rid of them in Rotterdam, Hamburg . . . but no one would have them,' said the Captain.

The stowaways remained on board for months, travelling to Jordan, Saudi Arabia, and Europe and back. If the *Minos* had arrived in a British port with stowaways on board, the company would be fined up to two thousand pounds a head.

I read an article in an old newspaper lining a drawer in my cabin, as if it had been placed there deliberately to warn me not to try and smuggle an African on board:

CAPTAIN BEAT ABANDONED STOWAWAYS

A Greek freighter captain beat two Kenyan stowaways before forcing them to jump overboard into shark-infested waters in the Indian Ocean.

'I watched the captain club two stowaways on the head as they screamed for mercy on their knees. The chief engineer fired a shotgun into the air to scare them and force them overboard,' said the second mate . . .

The captain had given the stowaways life jackets with the ship's name erased. They had perished off the Somalian coast.

'Serves them right,' said Jimmy when I told him what I had read in my drawer, displaying rare sympathy with the hated Greeks.

Jimmy was off the wagon: 'Once a stowaway's on board you're lumbered unless you send them over the side.'

We left for Tema on Morning watch. I leant over the deckrail at the stern and watched the land being sucked away down the narrowing estuary of River Cameroon until all that was left was the mud from the mangrove swamps discolouring the water. The seamen milled around the ship, glancing occasionally towards the open sea. Departures were popular.

The calm routine returned now we were once again in open waters and there were no unwelcome interruptions. The watches on the bridge returned to four hours on, eight hours off. We had a three-day sail to Tema.

'Where are we?' I asked Keith as he passed me on deck.

'Crossing five degrees north soon,' he answered.

That was not what I had meant at all. I meant where *were* we. Opposite Bonny? Off Cape Formoso? Close by the entrance to the Benin River? I measured our position from the nearest piece of solid earth.

Jimmy tapped on the porthole. 'Come in, come in,' he mouthed like a fish in a tank. 'I've got something for you.'

I was led to the purser's office. Jimmy unlocked a cupboard from the ring of keys hanging on a chain hooked to his belt and pulled out a white boilersuit from the top of a pile. This was Jimmy's slop chest. He lifted up the label.

'Forty-two. The smallest I've got. It'll have to do,' and he threw the white bundle at me. 'That's ten kni . . . ten quid,' he caught himself.

Bloody ridiculous, I thought. Why the hell won't Jimmy swear in front of me?

'But I don't want one. Thanks.' I put the boilersuit down on his desk. 'It's too big for me. But thanks anyway.'

'The lads pay a tenner, but I'll let you have it for eight. It's too small for most.' Jimmy was insistent.

At breakfast and dinner the officers appeared in the rig-of-the-day. But in between, in the engine room or down the hatches, they wore their boilersuits. Jimmy was offering me the seamen's working uniform.

I picked up the white bundle.

'OK. I'll take it then,' I said, trying to sound as if I had fallen for a bargain.

'Well,' Jimmy twitched his head to show me the door and moved to lock up the office, my initiation ceremony over. 'Better get back to the galley. The cook'll be nicking the fucking tea bags.'

I was learning, after what I would record in my log as The Boilersuit Incident, to expect no great statements from the seamen, no lowered eyes while emotional moments were shared, no open declarations of comradeship. They were just seamen, nothing more and nothing less.

When I appeared on the bridge in my boilersuit, Keith was on watch and Sissay at the wheel.

'Coffee?' The Second Mate was a tea-drinking man, as were all the officers, but the distilled water on board made rotten tea. Coffee tasted better.

'Bit big for you, that,' he said, placing the mug down on a ledge next to the wheel. I had hitched up the boilersuit with a belt and rolled up the arms and legs.

'Not bad, though. Can't tell who you are from behind. Could be a seaman,' and he laughed quietly to himself.

The First Mate came up on watch.

'She's yawing a bit,' he said with mild concern.

I ignored his remark, uncertain whether I should be worried, indifferent, or proud. The Mate walked over to the chart table.

'You can switch to auto,' he ordered. 'We're steering straight up past the Volta before turning in for Tema.'

Later I looked up 'YAW, to' in my shipping dictionary:

the effect on a ship's course produced by a following wind or sea. With the vessel travelling through the water in the same direction as that in which the sea is running or the wind blowing, the effect of the rudder is diminished and the vessel yaws away from the desired course. A good helmsman can often anticipate the moment when a vessel is most likely to yaw, and correct the tendency to do so by applying the requisite helm to counteract it. A yaw can also be caused by unintelligent steering on the part of a helmsman.

*

It was a great relief when the storm broke later that night. A sea voyage without a storm wouldn't really count. As we were sailing in the doldrums – the belt of calm lying between the equator and the trade winds – I was worried we might make the whole voyage without 'water on deck' as the Deck Log had promised.

The seamen didn't welcome a storm, although there was a gentle pride in the performance of the ship. From inside my cabin, it sounded as if a fire was raging as water cracked against the metal decks. I went out to receive my baptism. The sea rose in huge smooth sheets which shattered on the rails and swam about furiously at my feet. It was utterly black outside. Not the sight, but the noise showed the anger of the storm. The wind provided the bass in a sea symphony, invading every crevice to create a different pitch of roar. I expected to look up and see the moon vibrating from the force of the wind.

The phrase 'angry sea' seemed to sum up the raging water. Angry is a word usually attached to people. But when we describe the sea, we always ascribe it qualities – angry, calm, cruel – as if it had human moods.

The lightning lit up the angry sea more than daylight, but left it the steel grey of night water. I had read that the average depth of the ocean is estimated to be 12,500 feet, almost two and a half miles. Nine tenths of the world is covered by water. With these two figures the total volume of water can be calculated to be 329 million cubic miles. When I looked up 'sea' in *Roget's Thesaurus*, the first entry was 'great quantity'. The storm *was* enormous and the *Minos*, which had always seemed so big, felt small for the first time.

Second Mate Keith made the 1230 message over the tannoy the next day:

> Our noon position was 4°58′ North, 2°33′ East.
> We are 135 miles from Tema travelling at thirteen knots.
> Our Estimated Time of Arrival is 2300 hours.
> The clocks will be retarded half an hour at midnight.
> Repeat.
> The clocks will be retarded half an hour at midnight.

As we moved from port to port, we altered the clock in thirty-minute stages to adjust to the new time zone we would be entering. Any larger alterations would have meant an even longer watch would have had to be worked. As it was, Keith, on Middle watch from midnight to 0400 hours, would be on duty an extra half hour. But as a result of these gradual changes, we were seldom in any known time zone, but somewhere in between the one we had just left and the one we were sailing towards.

The engines were stopped at 0030 hours, twelve miles off Breaker Point. We waited for daylight and a pilot to guide us in to Tema, drifting slightly on a low sea. I adjusted the alarm clock beside the bed in my cabin. Time on the *Minos*, like everything else on board, made little sense once the gangway was lowered and you went ashore.

Chapter Six

No 1 Quay, Port of Tema

LATITUDE 5°37′ NORTH, LONGITUDE 0°01′ EAST

Jimmy told the agent wearing a fluorescent pink nylon shirt, that I was on board and would want to go into Accra, 'Though God knows why,' and the two men toasted my madness with Johnnie Walker in the purser's office.

Along the whole two thousand miles of the West African coast there are only two natural harbours – Dakar in Senegal, and Freetown in Sierra Leone. For four hundred years, from the fifteenth to the nineteenth century, this was no barrier to trade. The main business was in slaves, and humans were self-stowing cargo. A shrewd merchant would take into account a few lives lost in the surf when calculating his profits and losses. But when palm kernels replaced human cargo, surf boats had to be employed to take the goods out to the ships anchored off-shore. In Accra, the Customs had their own smart white surf boat with a crew in matching white uniforms and blue jumpers embroidered with HM Customs.

As trade boomed, channels were dredged and deepwater berths constructed all along the West African coast. By the 1970s, large liners could berth in Douala, Monrovia, Calabar, Port Harcourt and Bonny crude-oil loading terminal. But Accra, although the capital of Ghana, only had a small harbour with a maximum depth of six feet. The government still supplied surf boats, so a ship could anchor in the roads if she wished and her cargo be taken out to her, but nearly all vessels chose to dock fifteen miles east in the new artificial harbour at Tema.

New Tema, as the Ministries of Transport and Communications proudly called it, was opened in 1961 with the ambition of becoming the largest planned community on the African continent. New

Tema Development Corporation had built Community Number One, housing seventeen thousand in concrete apartment blocks; Community Number Two, overlooking the harbour, housed eight thousand. Now eleven purpose-built self-contained communities, each allotted a certain social status of residents, sprawl over the New Tema site with a population exceeding two hundred thousand. The former inhabitants of the old Tema, which had had a population of four thousand who lived by fishing, have been resettled in a planned village two miles away. The new Accra to Tema railway, opened by former President Dr Kwame Nkrumah, cut them off from the sea. But some continue to fish with drift nets from long wooden pirogues launched from the beach beside the harbour and peddle giant prawns to the ships in port.

It was Sunday in New Tema and ashore was still asleep. Two employees of the shipping line who ran the Tema office drove me along the coast road in a canvas hooded van with 'Liner Agencies Accra' painted on the side. I sat between the two men on the front seat. Tall silver-stemmed palm trees rustled in the sea breeze and fishing boats rotted into skeletons at irregular intervals along the white sand.

The drive to Accra was slow and quiet for a West African journey. The two Ga agents spoke little English and I spoke no Ga. I tried a list of place names. I started where I had started: Nigeria.

'Nigeria,' the one at the wheel repeated. 'Nigeria.'

The force with which he spat out the word was international. Nigeria was not his favourite place.

'Nigerians. Guns. Thieves. Armed robbers,' offered his friend, finding words in an unfamiliar language through his strength of feeling. His head shook purposefully and tongue took to clicking violently. It was as if a mechanical doll had suddenly been wound up.

I worked my way up the coast.

'Togo.'

The clicking stopped and a long sigh emitted from the passenger's slowly shaking head.

'To-go.' The man at the wheel drew out the two syllables slowly, as if lamenting someone long since dead. 'Togo. No more.'

'Today,' said his friend, pointing with his finger at a spot on the windscreen in front of him as if geographically locating the hour. 'Today, Togo like Nigeria.'

He was pleased with the comparison.

The driver smiled and nodded several times in agreement.

'Ghana,' I said.

There was a moment of silence.

'Ghana,' repeated the driver with an almost whimsical air, as if remembering a lost love.

His friend tried to articulate. 'Nigeria come to Ghana. Thieves. Guns.'

The driver threw him a disapproving look. 'Ghana good. Ghana good.'

'Accra Cathedral!' cried his friend, suddenly cheered by a bright new idea.

The driver pressed his foot down on the pedal, eager to reach the religious magnificence.

'It's old?' I asked as we turned into the city centre. I hoped it would be the same building Mary Kingsley had visited while under construction in 1895.

'Old. Very old,' said the friend, so glad he could please.

The Ga, a largely Christian people, observe the sabbath. As we drove to the cathedral, the only hawkers were small boys balancing large trays of bruised orange mangoes on their heads. We arrived at what I presumed to be a Muslim Sunday market.

'Accra Cathedral!' cheered the driver, pointing at a square concrete tower rising up behind the crowds of squatting women who were busy wrapping up tiny parcels of kola nuts in newspaper for the churchgoers. Everyone was in his or her Sunday best, with the men wearing their kentes, brightly coloured material decorated with spirals and worn like a toga with the loose end thrown over the left shoulder. The cathedral's concrete gleamed a ghastly white amongst all the browns, greens and oranges of the people. It was also violently vertical, thrusting skywards, not sprawling and softly clinging to the earth like the surrounding buildings. A plaque built into its façade indicated that it had been built in 1974.*

---

*I was convinced by the Ga men that I was seeing the most important religious edifice in Accra. Now I discover this building was no cathedral at all, but just a minor church in the city, presumably one to which the driver and his friend belonged.

The driver pointed at the plaque, beaming and nodding.

'It's beautiful,' I lied.

Our tour continued to the National Museum guarded by a metal figure of Ghana's first President, the pan-Africanist philosopher Kwame Nkrumah who was thrown from power by a coup while on a peace mission to Hanoi in 1966 and died in exile six years later. Once his statue had stood near Black Star Square in front of the Parliament Buildings. Now its arms had been chopped off. I snapped the statue nervously, anxious that it might be considered an offence, but the two Ga agents just nodded and grinned.

In Post Office Square, I snapped the giant poster of sunglassed Flight Lieutenant Jerry Rawlings, the half-Scottish military Head of State, the ninth since Nkrumah, holding up a clenched fist under the slogan 'Build the Peoples Defence Committees Into Organs of the Peoples Power'.

Another government poster advertised Foreign Exchange Shop. I asked the driver's friend what they sold.

'Special things,' he said.

'What kind of special things?'

'Rice.'

'What else is there to see in Accra?' I inquired.

We went for a beer.

'BU-BRA AVAILABLE. 60 CEDIS PINT' read the notice at the roadside shack. We sat in silence among rows of wooden brooms for sale. The landlady unrolled rush mats in the corner and put two pot-bellied children to sleep for the afternoon. The young boy lying curled on his side stared out between the fingers of his cupped hand. I winked, and he clapped his fingers back over his eyes.

We emptied our glasses and drove back along the coast road. The dark came suddenly, so I could only hear the surf and the chattering palm trees and only see the water when it was caught by the moon. I watched every shiver among the leaves in case it was caused by an armed robber, and started when a bush rat with a long heavy body and tiny thin legs scuttled out across the road in front of us.

Part of the strain of my months spent in Nigeria had been the constant knowledge that I might die, any moment, and for no particular reason. Even travelling by car had been a great danger; you are forty-two times more likely to die in a car crash in Nigeria than in Britain. Import restrictions have made rubber tyres unob-

tainable, and the worn rims frequently burst, through a combination of the heat and potholed roads. Their black rubber fragments
litter the highways, and car crashes have overtaken malaria as the
most common cause of premature death.

Once I had seen the results of a crash in Kano – a brain, just a brain,
lying in the street, popped out from the skull like a pea from a pod.
The body, teenage and male, was sprayed thinly on the other side of
the road. Notices used to appear outside the departmental offices at
the University of Ibadan announcing yet another member of staff
had died in a 'ghastly accident' – 'ghastly' was the favoured adjec-
tive. Students crowded round to see if it was anyone they knew.

Driving at night was even more perilous. Along the Ibadan to
Lagos highway, armed robbers were on patrol. Nigerians seldom
drove in the dark, and I had learnt to be afraid. I thought the two Ga
men must be crazy taking such a risk as driving us along the unlit
coast road. I had bought a broom in the BU-BRA bar which I propped
up against the back seat next to me and calculated could be used as a
club.

I was thankful to see the gates of the dock and be back on board.
The *Minos*, nestling in her own time zone, was a haven.

The ship was now working to in-port periods of duty, the engineers on
from about seven in the morning to five in the afternoon, while the
mates, if they were not wanted at the hatches, could go ashore. No
one did. Instead they wrote up their notes, caught up on any office
work in their cabins, and hung around in the bar. The following
evening I watched the lights from the dock being switched on
through my cabin porthole. The phone rang. It was Roger, excited.

'There are seven British Caledonian airhostesses in the bar if you
fancy a bit of female company. Why don't you come down?'

I muttered a listless 'Great', and replaced the receiver.

'Women,' I tutted, plonking myself down heavily on the bed. I had
grown used to sitting amongst the men in the evenings, drinking too
much beer and listening to their tales.

'Women! What do they want coming on board?'

I was sitting in my knickers and an 'I am Proud to be a Farmer' T-
shirt which I had exchanged for a pair of stars and stripes socks while
waiting for the minibus in Douala motopark. I snatched up my
boilersuit from the bed, pulled it up over my shoulders and tied it

with a belt. I wiggled my Wet 'n' Wild toe-nails. This could be considered trendy, I thought. I looked in the mirror and liked what I saw.

The officers' saloon was always smoky.

'Hey, come on over,' Roger shouted, waving an arm already beginning to have a life of its own. He was struggling with the cellophane on a carton of beer cans, simultaneously trying to entertain the two women on the other side of the bar.

'This is Shirley. And this is – ' he smiled, too familiar already, he thought, for any offence to be taken by the mere forgetting of a name.

Two heads turned and smiled at me, one brunette, one blonde.

'Dea,' Roger gestured with the flat palm of his spare hand as if a priest offering me up as the host. 'This is Dea. She's sailing with us. Beer?'

He ripped out a can for me. I pulled the ring and swigged exaggeratedly back. Shirley and her friend took a sip from urine-coloured drinks.

'Sorry about the ice.' Roger had been staring at the bronzed cleavage in front of which Shirley innocently held her glass. 'Don't usually get a call for it,' he remarked, as if the patron of some upmarket hotel caught out by a particularly discerning customer.

A glance around the bar revealed more Shirleys, all, except one, very pretty. Their hair was long, their nails long, their bare tanned legs impossibly long in high heels. They all looked so happy. They appeared to be a herd of strange animals, of an entirely different species to my own. I saw grotesquely painted exaggerated lips, scarlet talons on the end of creeper-like arms.

'Our plane is grounded at Accra,' explained Shirley. 'We're waiting for the bit to be flown out.'

As I looked around the bar, careful not to rest on any one face, white glossy smiles were flashed at me. The officers were in their 'Tropics'. A woman loves a uniform, they had calculated. The smell of smoke mingled with the fruit cocktail of the officers' stolen avocado and mango lotions.

Drinks and cigarettes were being plied gallantly upon the girls, accepted in moderation. If I hadn't seen a white woman since Sarah, the officers had been starved of white female company for two months. But while the women's eyes flirted, their backs stayed straight, refusing to accommodate the contorted shapes of the officers' bodies bending to almost – but never actually – touch their scented female forms.

I was a spectator to this sport. I was angry and upset. I was just, maybe, being accepted by these men. Now these women – these *women* – had come along and reminded them that I, too, was female. They could go back to their fancy Ghanaian Hilton that night. This was where I lived.

'Dea – over here, meet Sandy,' called Doug.

Sandy smiled. I strolled over and put the can of beer down just too heavily on the table, slouched a little low into the chair, and sat with my legs parted wide. I remained silent, smiling.

'What's it like to be amongst all these men?' Sandy enquired.

I ignored her polite enquiry and picked up my can.

'Got a cig, Doug?' I bellowed, throwing out further signs of my assimilation. 'Did you see the *Princess Bothnia* as we came in?'

Doug threw me the packet. I detected Avocado Shower Gel as he waved his arm. He continued to explain the intricate, technical tasks of a radio officer to Sandy.

'You see, we're responsible for the safety of the ship and the men, in the end. I mean, if anyone is sick or there's any sort of emergency, I have to send the messages and contact other ships and stations. There's channel sixteen, you see, that's on the emergency distress frequency and it's kept open all the time. When you . . .'

Sandy, whose working days were spent wafting down the aisles of a jumbo jet, nodded politely.

'What is it like to be the only woman among all these men?' she persisted, throwing a wide theatrical glance around the bar, sweeping mascaraed eyes over the dozen half-drunk officers, average age forty-five, their bellies already straining the starched white shirts of their Tropics.

'It's fine,' I offered, throwing off her enquiry lightly. 'They're very good to me.'

I wished I had either taken out my Little English Number dress or ironed a pair of decent trousers. It wasn't so much that I was neither male nor female, but I was underdressed for whichever I was.

Doug broke his gaze from Sandy's face.

'Oh, she's not a woman,' he grinned, dismissing the thought as if an animal, tree or the funnel of a passing ship had been incorrectly catalogued by an amateur observer. 'She's Jella. She's one of us. You see, channel sixteen must always be kept clear, so as soon as . . . '

By the time I left for my cabin that evening I had drunk and danced the night away, partnering Fourth Engineer Steve to Michael Jackson and Shirley to Joan Armatrading. As I swayed past the Captain's cabin, the Old Man came out carrying a bucket of soapy water. Every evening he washed his bathroom floor and emptied the dirty suds over the side of the ship. His shorts showed off blue-white legs capped by bedroom slippers, furry inside, tartan outside. He nodded good evening to me, his neighbour, and hobbled back home, clicking his front door behind him.

Chapter Seven

At Sea

LATITUDE 5°37′ NORTH, LONGITUDE 0°01′ EAST TO
LATITUDE 6°21′ NORTH, LONGITUDE 10°48′ WEST

It was good to be at sea again, away from the airhostesses and anxieties on land. By breakfast we had cleared Accra Point. I went to look for Billy on the bridge.

'What does "Jella" mean?'

Sissay, standing at the wheel, laughed two little separate laughs, barely distinguishable from a cough.

I went to find Jimmy in the galley.

'Who's Jella?' I asked George. The Chief Cook gave a long, amused sigh.

'You're Jella.'

'I know I'm Jella. But *how*? What's Jella? What does it mean?' I said exasperated.

Jimmy's belly was vibrating as he leant back against the counter and took another draw on his cigarette.

'It's the crew's language,' he said. 'It's their word for small boy. It's what they call you – the Africans. It's like an apprentice, cadet. Something like that.'

He continued to chuckle.

'Why do they call me a boy?'

'Well you're not very womanly are you,' he said and George giggled as Jimmy ran his hands in curves which flowed in the opposite direction to his own wide-waisted body.

'And you're trying to be a seaman. Seamen are men. Male. Masc-u-line. Oga. Master. That right, George?' he turned to his cook.

George released a whispery titter like a balloon going down.

'Except you're rather a little one. Only learning.'

The two other apprentices on board – the Mexican cadets Ramiro and Jesus – were much taller than me. They were both just turned twenty, dark-skinned and skimpy. They acted like teenagers together, always getting excited about things, two frisky puppies amongst a litter of tired old dogs. They took everything that was said at face value, as if it was meant in earnest, and the British seamen's cynicism was lost on them.

Ramiro and Jesus were on secondment from a small Mexican shipping line; in return for the guarantee of a contract to maintain the Mexican line's fleet, our shipping line had agreed to train Mexican cadets. They ate at the junior officers' table and kept to themselves in the bar, Ramiro chattering away in Spanish to Jesus who responded with short nods and mild gestures with his hands.

'What does he talk to you about?' I asked Jesus.

'Oh, he tells me of his country, of his family in Mexico City, of his brothers, of his mother, of his girlfriend. He talks about his sister's children. He is very homesick.'

Ramiro and Jesus had spent six months of their two-year seatime with the shipping line.

'Hey, Denis.' Keith always called Ramiro Denis. He said it was the English translation of Ramiro. No one ever talked to or about Jesus, so he was able to keep the name his mother gave him.

'Hey, Denis. This is a British ship you know. Only English is spoken on this ship,' Keith shouted at Ramiro one evening as he chatted away in front of the passive Jesus. Ramiro looked up, his dark face twitching at the unkindness, then turned back to Jesus and continued talking in a hush. The British officers were resentful that the shipping line no longer trained British cadets for officer positions.

Just outside Tema we crossed from the eastern to the western hemisphere, and our noon position was 5°03' North, 0°45' West.

Tema is almost due south of Liverpool on the Greenwich meridian, 2870 nautical miles as the crow flies. But the great bulbous head of Africa protrudes over one thousand nautical miles to the west and has to be rounded before making east through the North Atlantic and the Bay of Biscay, adding half as much again to the length of a voyage.

Our next port of call, Monrovia, capital of the Republic of

Liberia, was approximately seventy hours away. Liberia was the homeland of the Kru people. They had originally lived on the coast of Cape Palmas in the south-east of the country, bordering the Côte d'Ivoire. Excellent sailors, they paddled their canoes made from a single burnt-out trunk, taking off their wrappers and winding them around their heads, naked but keeping their clothes dry. With the foundation of the Province of Freedom in Sierra Leone in the late eighteenth century, a model colony for freed American slaves, Kru migrated to Freetown to work on the Sierra Leone Company's ships and at the wharf. Now as many Kru live in Sierra Leone as Liberia, and an area of Freetown is officially called Kru Town. Most of our crew came from there.

The shipping line had employed them as sailors, cooks, stewards and firemen to the engines since the 1870s. At sea, the Kru had shared quarters with the Europeans and were paid the same wages. Shipboard segregation arrived in the 1890s, when separate living areas were introduced and different rates of pay for the British officers and the 'Kruboys'. When an office was opened to recruit them directly in Freetown, their names even disappeared from the British Crew Agreement. In the official records held by the Board of Trade which show who worked the ship, there is no mention of the crew. It reads as if she sailed without any stewards, cooks, lookouts, chipping gang, engine-room hands or steersmen. Today, seamen on British ships who were recruited abroad are still exempt from the Race Relations Act.

On the *Minos*, the crew quartered on the deck below the officers, who quartered on the deck below the Captain and myself. Quartering in the cabin marked PILOT next to the cabin marked MASTER, I was under the Old Man's protection. This meant any attempts to muck in with the men came under close scrutiny, for I could be the Old Man's spy. No one ventured into our deck except the Old Man and I, and the Old Man was a canny one. Who knows what information was exchanged between us.

My invitation to the Captain's cabin for a drink at Apapa was commented upon regularly in the bar.

'The officers' deck not good enough for you? Why don't you take your beer to the Old Man's cabin? Don't want to sit around with us riff raff,' jeered Roger who, as Chief Engineer, was the most regular visitor to the cabin marked MASTER.

'There's a spare cabin next to mine,' shouted Keith across the bar. 'But it's got "cadet" on the door. And you're a *pilot* aren't you.'

The men laughed.

The *Minos* was a strictly ordered, enclosed world. The divisions between junior and senior officers, and between officers and crew, had been established for decades. But my position on board was not as clear cut. I was technically not an officer but a member of crew. 'D. Birkett, Miss' appeared between Sissay and Bonoh on the crew list pinned outside the purser's office. Officers and cadets were listed on a separate sheet. But I ate and drank with the officers, and the crew ate and drank in their own mess and bar. I asked Jimmy what the crew had for lunch.

'Pepper soup,' he said. 'Monday chicken pepper soup. Tuesday fish pepper soup. Wednesday vegetable pepper soup. Thursday beef pepper soup. And Friday chicken pepper soup again. They love pepper soup. Live on the stuff.'

'Quite like it myself,' I said. 'Can I eat with the crew sometime?'

Jimmy turned over my request suspiciously. I could miss meals, as he did, but if I was going to eat I had to do so in the place allotted to me on board. That was opposite Roger and between Doug and the Mate on the Old Man's table.

'No,' said Jimmy. 'It's not on.'

'But I am crew,' I pleaded. 'I'm only a steersman. I even have a West African name.'

'You're British,' said Jimmy.

'I'm also an apprentice.'

Jimmy paced up and down the few yards of his galley and played a rhythm with his fingers on the counters.

'It's chicken pepper soup tomorrow,' he said. 'That's the best one. You can have some of that.'

I didn't realise what a hot issue enjoying a bowl of pepper soup would be. The following lunchtime I walked through the officers' mess to the galley and out the other side to reach the crew's mess.

'Why didn't you come through the crew's mess door?' hissed Jimmy.

'Didn't think of it.'

'Jesus.'

Half a dozen of the crew were already halfway through their pepper soup. George ladled out a bowl from the giant saucepan and handed it over the counter to me. The one long table was bare except for bowls and spoons. There was no tablecloth covering the wood-vinyl top and no place settings for each man. I sat down where there was a space. The man sitting next to me nodded and continued to drink the red oily liquid. I didn't recognise anyone except a man I thought was Quist, but I wasn't sure. He'd been outside on lookout one night when I was on the bridge with Billy.

The soup was good. It smelt pungent and large pieces of chicken bobbed up and down in it. The men tackled them by putting whole pieces, including the bones, into their mouths then spitting the stripped carcass out in small fragments on to the table.

'You like pepper soup?'

'Yes, sir,' I replied. If I had to call the older officers 'sir' when I replied to their questions, I didn't see why I shouldn't show the same respect to a member of crew.

Quist clicked his tongue, tapped the side of the table with his free hand, and spat out a bone.

'Eeeeh. You learn quick, seester.'

The men all tapped the table or clicked their tongues in agreement, then returned to their conversation in a language I didn't understand.

One of the earliest European commentators on the Kru, Thomas Winterbottom MD, physician to the colony of Sierra Leone, had recorded in 1803 that the Kru language has 'a guttural, singing pronunciation, which is very disagreeable'. Dr Winterbottom's *Account of the Native Africans of the Neighbourhood of Sierra Leone to Which is Added an Account of the Present State of Medicine Among Them* is a gripping read, with the index directing the reader to such intriguing topics as 'Navel, prodigiously enlarged', 'Nostalgia, not peculiar to Switzerland', 'Sailors, become sooner infirm than any other classes of men', and 'Venereal disease, generally introduced by Europeans'.

Despite his reservations about the language, as all Europeans Dr Winterbottom had admired the Kru seamen. They were, he wrote, 'remarkable for the robustness and fleshiness of their bodies, and also for their great agility.' Our Captain, who risked being called a 'coolie master' by other commanding officers who sailed routes with British ratings, had once announced, 'Sail with Africans rather than those unionised whites. Any day.'

Lunch in the crew's mess was soon over. It seemed a very trivial thing to have done, and I wondered why I had thought it so important to push Jimmy into allowing me to eat with the crew.

I sat bronzing on deck reading Jack London's *The Sea Wolf*. Some hills were just visible on a far-off coast. The Captain had given me an old deckchair stored in his cabin, left behind by an earlier captain's wife. Now the shipping line no longer allowed wives to travel with their husbands, to save on costs.

The Sea Wolf was not a cheering story. It seemed to be about the confusion a woman brings to a working boat, through no fault of her own. Captain Wolf Larsen was a tyrannical but efficient master and Humphrey Van Weyden a reluctant but increasingly competent seaman. The stresses and strains between the professional officer and his gentleman mate were kept in check as they went about working the ship. Then a shipwrecked Miss Maud Brewster arrives and the fine balance on board is thrown awry. The captain falls in love with Miss Maud. The gentleman mate tries to defend her honour. The two men are now rivals for the lady's affection. Mr Humphrey Van Weyden is forced to challenge the Wolf's authority in his bid to save Miss Brewster from his superior officer's advances. Shipboard discipline crumbles. The captain descends through madness to death. Mr Van Weyden and Miss Brewster are stranded on a desert island. The tragic consequences of having a woman on board seemed limitless.

At least there was no question of the Old Man throwing down his bowl of sudsy water and grasping me to him in his tartan slippers. But perhaps I did threaten the order on board. Most societies have a word for strangers which they apply indiscriminately. In Northern Nigeria, the Hausa call you *bature*. In Yorubaland, the word is *oyibo*. In Bonny I had been called *amingo*; it didn't matter whether I was English, Portuguese or American, or even coffee-coloured rather than white, I would still have been given that name. It literally meant 'friend', but it really meant 'outsider'.

A ship, however, is such a closed society that it doesn't even have a word for an intruder – there never are any. Everyone has a title, usually embossed upon his cabin door; PURSER, MASTER, CHIEF OFFICER, BOATSWAIN, COOK. His place on board is clear; there is no question about it.

The seamen needed to find a place for me. Otherwise, like Miss Maud Brewster, my mere presence as an uncategorised outsider would threaten to undermine the order of the ship. I had come to be grateful for the boilersuit – at least I hardly looked like a woman any more. The crew had come up with a name. Things seemed to be working out nicely. But to the officers, and to Fourth Engineer Steve in particular, I was still a young woman called Dea.

Steve was twenty-three years old and had been at sea five years. He had first joined a ship as a teenage cadet. He was presented with his seaman's certificate in the last year that the shipping line had trained British cadets, and the Sixth Engineer was the most junior member of crew. Steve was bright and capable, and soon promoted. He moved to a more modern vessel as Fifth Engineer – but there had been no Sixth. On the *Minos*, there were only four engineers. I joked one night that his nickname should be 'Lowest of the Low': he was always stuck on the bottom rung of the ladder.

The joke was not very funny. There was no doubt that Steve was good at his job, and the other men knew it. He would have made an excellent chief engineer. But now that position seemed hopelessly remote, and Steve could not help but resent it. It was as if fate had decided to deny him his rightful place in this strictly ordered society afloat.

He hoped to find some understanding from me, another person without a proper place. As long as I too was an outsider, we could be allies. The Fourth Engineer was the only seaman who had ever approached me when I was alone. He was disappointed in my boilersuit and persisted in calling me Dea. I felt closer to him than any of the other officers. Yet Steve was also my greatest threat. Unlike him, I didn't mind being at the bottom of the pile as long as I was included. I just wanted to be Jella, one of the men. I wanted everything to stay exactly as it was, but let me in.

But without realising it, I had already placed myself in danger of being ostracised.

'Did you enjoy your pepper soup?' Roger asked in the bar that night, smug in the news he was imparting to the men. 'Bit hot for you, was it?'

I took my beer over to Doug.

'Shouldn't do that,' he said.

'Shouldn't do what?'

'You know. Eat with the crew.'

'Why the hell not?'

'It's not done. You're British. You eat with the officers. End of conversation,' and he threw me a cigarette.

It was a very long night in the bar. I had somehow disrupted the normal easy atmosphere of the evenings, and no one spoke much. We watched a video called *On the Lone Plain*, a loud Western with lots of drawling voices and stirring music. The men seemed to like it.

When the credits rolled, I swigged back what was left of my beer and was about to leave, when someone suggested, 'Let's have one of those other films.'

The officers glanced about at each other, and cocked their heads towards me. It seemed that my earlier transgression would be written off, just this once, and I was to be given another chance. The seamen relaxed back into their swivel chairs.

'OK. I'm for it,' said Jimmy, off the wagon.

'Oh, put it on, then,' said Doug. 'What the hell,' and flashed me a hopeful smile.

Those things which on land I would have taken offence to, I hoped for on the ship. I was flattered when the men swore in my company, and took the greeting 'It's bloody Jella' when I walked into the bar as a great compliment. I sensed that I was about to be honoured even more.

The film began. *Trouble Down Below* contained little plot but a great number of groans and barrels of naked flesh. *On the Lone Plain* was the last Western we watched, and normal transmission resumed for the rest of the voyage.

The last thing I would remember each night as I slipped into bed was the honest picture of a naked woman, legs akimbo on a couch, staring at me from the TV screen in the officers' saloon.

Chapter Eight

Commercial Quay, Monrovia

LATITUDE 6°21' NORTH, LONGITUDE 10°48' WEST

Three days out from Tema we were alongside Monrovia docks.

Second Mate Keith reported sick with feverish symptoms, and malaria was suspected. As the agent would be driving him in to town to see a doctor, I asked if I could go along for the ride. We would probably turn around in less than a day; we only had to load empty containers. But I was certain that I would know everything interesting or important about Liberia after a quick excursion ashore.

I had soon become accustomed to summing up a country and its people in a few hours away from the ship. Chance encounters and snatches of conversation defined how I would remember a port of call. In Buea, the responsibility for my impressions of Cameroon had rested with a twelve-year-old child. I had liked Peter, so thought Cameroonians were lovely people and had said so many times in the officers' saloon.

'Great place, Cameroon,' I'd say. 'People are really friendly. They have this funny thing about taking photographs though. They don't mind you taking a photo of them, but they don't like you doing it of the buildings. Kind of touchy about it.'

In Accra, the two Ga agents had been representative voices for the Ghanaian nation. All Ghanaians, I now truly believed, thoroughly distrusted other West Africans and thought they would rob them.

I only needed to accidentally attach myself to a lunatic in Monrovia, and the total two million Liberian population would be, as far as I was concerned, deranged. The seamen, who rarely ventured off the quay, were just the same. For them, shoreworkers came to represent a whole country, so when it was discovered that the containers had been broken into in Douala, all Cameroonians were thieves.

Keith sagged in the back of the agent's silver Mercedes, sweating and whimpering. I sat in the front with the windows closed, the air-conditioning on, and American soul music pounding from the stereo. I lay back and looked through the windscreen at the wide boulevard as if watching a film. The market women scurried across the screen, their bodies as taut as clefs, balancing trays of matches, mangoes and kola nuts on their heads. We crossed a bridge out from the ramshackle suburbs of corrugated iron houses into the centre of town. Monrovia lies at the end of a long thin spit, only just connected to the land, and the town centre rests on top of the hill with roads sloping down on all sides to the sea.

'CHASE MANHATTAN PLAZA' a sign in the middle of the road read, and I repeated the words out loud.

'You know it?' asked the agent. 'See that tall building? That tall one?'

He pointed to a four storey office block. It had CHASE MANHATTAN BANK in large letters on the front.

I watched Keith shake off the agent's arm as he walked through the gate to the surgery, and wandered off by myself up a curved street. Burgers were painted, oozing from their buns, on café windows.

In 1822, the American Colonisation Society, wanting to rid the United States of freed slaves, shipped them to Liberia. Those who agreed to leave were strict Christians: they were on a mission to bring civilisation to Africa. They modelled their new society on the land they had left, basing their constitution on that of the USA and calling their seat of government the Capitol.

The black settlers proved as good masters as the European colonialists. They imposed forms of forced labour on the indigenous people akin to slavery, and sold this labour to the Spanish in Fernando Po. They grabbed and tenaciously maintained political and economic power. By the middle of this century, the Voice of America was transmitting from Monrovia throughout Africa, and Liberia was promoted as a bastion of anti-communism in a continent which was flirting with socialist alternatives. The US dollar was legal tender. The Liberian dollar, looking exactly the same except for the word 'Liberian' printed on it, had a street value a quarter of that of the official US–Liberian one-to-one exchange rate.

Liberia was one of the few English-speaking West African countries to continue to attract a substantial tourist trade. Young Americans were wandering around the hilly streets of Monrovia with little pouches on their belts like codpieces, in which they hid their US dollars.

The main street was lined with displays of tie-dye, leatherwork and brass. 'Hi. How yer doing?' a stallholder cried out. Tall-ceilinged rooms opened on to the road, whirring with overhead fans and the sound of rows of small boys pedalling away at treadle sewing machines. Bundles of cloth lay about the floor, to be sewn up and embroidered for kaftans and draw-string trousers for the visitors.

In one shop I saw a blond American wearing cut-off denims taking a tape measure out of his codpiece and laying it against a short kaftan.

'It's for a small woman,' he was telling one of the boys.

'Yes, small small,' the boy agreed, holding up the dress to show off the blistering orange tie-dyed sun with a deep red centre where the small woman's belly button would be. 'See.'

The blond American did not see. The dress was as wide as it was long. African women aren't concerned with a snug fit, but let their breasts – banging and flopping around under the wealth of fabric – play with the pattern.

It was late afternoon and the shops were beginning to close. Outside one storefront stood two Lebanese, a father and son, watching a young African pull and push at the padlock which secured the metal shutters over the glass shop front. He was struggling with the key.

This scene repeated itself up the curve of the dimming street. Outside Aga's General Store and Zaruk's Chemist one old and one young Lebanese watched an African rattling the shutters. I would remember Liberia as a country which sold oversized tie-dye dresses to American tourists and was continually shutting-up shop.

I had told the agent I would find my own way back and hailed a cab, jumping into an empty vehicle. We sped along without stopping. It was forty cents and I had it all to myself; apparently you do not share taxis in Monrovia. I gave the driver a dollar, and he immediately gave me sixty cents change. Liberians, I deduced, are a thoroughly honest people.

At the gate to the port a group of men sat in a hut playing cards. I asked if one of them would walk me to the *Minos*. I felt like strolling back in African company, but I told them it was because I was afraid of the dark. One of the men without a uniform said he would go with me.

He chatted away about his homeland to the east, his job as a clerk in the Ministry of Transport, and his friend the port official he was visiting in the hut, and told me that, like ninety-five per cent of Liberians, he was Kru.*

'So you're a Kruboy!' I cried. I had heard the phrase used so often.

'I am not a boy,' he replied in the most gentle reproach. 'I am thirty-two years of age.'

The Kru people have always been independently minded and stubbornly resisted attempts at reformation and betterment of 'native races'. They were the last among the Liberian peoples to submit to conquest by the black settlers. Evangelism amongst them failed, and they refused to learn to read and write. The Methodist church opened in Kru Town in 1840, but had no converts. No nineteenth-century account mentions one christian-ised Kru.

Although agreeing to work for the slave-masters, it was believed that it was impossible to make the Kru themselves slaves. Schemes to plant them as indentured labour in the West Indies foundered. David Livingstone recruited a dozen Kru to man the launch on his 1858 Zambezi expedition, but when they later refused to act as his bearers on land, the missionary dismissed them back to Freetown. Working as navvies on the Panama Canal, they went on strike, demanding to be repatriated. They were, they said downing tools, ill-fed and dying. Only working the sea suited them.

We reached the ship, her steel ramparts towering above us. I knew it was not possible for me to return the Kru man's courtesy with the offer of a drink. No African ever set foot in the officers' saloon, and I did not even know where the crew's bar was, or if they had one.

*Official statistics state approximately two per cent of the Liberian population is Kru.

'Thanks a lot,' I said, grabbing his hand and shaking it violently. 'Thanks a lot. Very kind of you.'

The Kru was very gentlemanly, and decided to give me another chance. He muttered something about wanting to see his cousin. His cousin was a cook on a Liverpool vessel, perhaps he was our cook, he suggested politely.

I pretended I hadn't heard and walked briskly up the gangway, nodding as I passed Sissay on sentry at the top. Just behind me, I heard him stop the Kru. I walked on, my footsteps synchronised with the rattle of the Kru man descending to the dock.

The strip light above the desk in my cabin drowned out the lights from land.

Why are these people even polite to us?

was the only entry in my log that night.

The grey Mercedes drew up with a bundle of letters. Jimmy wandered about the ship handing them out. I had one with magnificent stamps smothering the whole envelope, depicting the Monument de L'Unité of the United Republic of Cameroon. The letter inside was folded into the shape of a butterfly whose wings moved if you pulled them apart. It was from Peter, my Mount Cameroon guide:

Dea
I'm Peter Bokwe from Buea Cameroon.
First of all I will ask of your conditional health in general. How do you had any complain?
This month is the month of rain and same so in your country too. What are you doing in England are you working or still in school learning. I have been hearing about England but I do not know it and how it look like. I want you to inform me about England. I want to know what time you will come here again.
I wish you god blessing to have a better job for your future and for your family and me too. So say hello to your family. Nex time I will write more about myself and my brother.
It's from me.
Peter.
P.S. Take over my mistakes.

I still don't know how Peter's letter reached me in Monrovia. The Liverpool office acted as a forwarding agency for mail, and all letters had to be addressed there, from where they were sent out to the agent at the next port of call. Peter must have handed his letter to the agent in Douala who had sent it direct to Monrovia, knowing we would dock there in about eight days' time.

But it still didn't make sense, because communications between West African countries are so poor. All the roads and railways, built by colonial administrations only interested in linking their imperial possession with the motherland, run from the interiors to the coasts. The railway from Lagos runs six hundred and eighty miles north to Nguru, thirty miles before the Niger border, and eight hundred miles east to Maiduguri, sixty miles from Cameroon. Neighbouring states Benin and Togo, both less than eighty miles wide, each have over three-hundred-mile-long railways that wiggle up into their interiors, but no line that crosses between the two countries. The line from Monrovia runs west through the Bomi Hills and stops abruptly at the border with Sierra Leone. In the whole of West Africa, there is not one railway which crosses from one West African coastal state to another.

Even by sea the journey is difficult. Ferries used to run between south-eastern Nigeria and south-western Cameroon, but these ceased a few years ago when border disputes erupted.

For a while I expected to find Peter hiding between the containers or locked in the ship's library (no larger than a cupboard) and was worried I might be thought to have harboured him as a stowaway. I even once checked behind my shower curtain, convinced his diminutive adult's body would pop out and announce, 'We have not seen the engine room.'

It was my last chance to post a letter home, so I scribbled a few comforting lines to the effect that I was feeling better than I had for months, my cabin was very comfortable, and the men were treating me very well, and handed it to the agent.

The land grew darker and the lights stronger. Ashore no longer interested me.

That same night, we slipped away from Africa.

Part II

At Sea

Chapter Nine

Lying in bed, I could look through the window at the water. As the ship rolled, the sea and sky seesawed in the metal window frame.

The porthole was made of two layers of strengthened glass screwed down with large nuts and bolts. It cut me off entirely from the endless swish of the waves. I could get up, wash and make my way to mess by the internal alleys and companionways without ever knowing I was at sea.

It was three weeks since I had joined the *Minos*. We were pointing towards the North Atlantic, the roughest ocean in the world and as large as Africa. It was 3216 nautical miles to Liverpool, our home port. I had travelled from Douala to Monrovia along the West African coast, and was 1535 nautical miles from my point of embarkation at Apapa. Yet in a sense I wasn't travelling anywhere. Wherever I went the *Minos* went too, and all her rules, customs and inhabitants. I was leading a remarkably sedentary life.

In the old atlas in the ship's library which marked shipping routes, a spidery purple thread stretched between Lagos and Liverpool. It looked like a vein across the ocean. The chilly north-west coast of England and the tropical West Coast of Africa always used to be joined on the maps in this way. Along this vein cotton, palm products, tin and iron ore travelled from West Africa. In Britain it was woven, boiled, and smelted. Bales of cloth, cartons of soap, saucepans and hurricane lamps travelled back along the line to West Africa.

The *Minos* was following this thread between the two continents. On my way to breakfast, I hung over the stern deckrail and watched our wake plough up the surface of the sea. As we set out for the ocean, we rattled with empty containers and half-filled holds. We could have stacked seven hundred containers in the holds and on deck, but we were carrying less than four hundred. Over three hundred of these were empty, simply being shuffled back to their owners in Britain. We were also loaded with a thousand tons of timber, raw cocoa beans, sacks of coffee and some sliced veneer, but were still carrying under half our full capacity. Now the vein was more of a haemorrhage than a lifeline, and the *Minos* was slowly bleeding to death.

The *Minos* and the men who worked her knew that she was one of the last of her line, but she still sailed proudly through the ocean with her freshly painted deckrails gleaming in the early sun, her red ensign cracking in a force five wind, her Captain stern on the bridge, the Chief Engineer hunched over the lights in the control room, the First Mate in his cabin writing up his notes, and the Chief Steward bawling out his Chief Cook in the galley.

'Lovely morning,' announced the Captain as I sat down at the breakfast table. Then as if it followed, 'Apapa is a terrible place.'

Only Doug was at mess.

'Full of,' and the Captain dipped his head towards his porridge. 'Thieving.'

It was the first time the Old Man had mentioned Africa.

I went up on the bridge to put in an extra hour towards my Steering Certificate.

'All yours,' said Sissay. 'Course 293.'

'293,' I repeated, and took the wheel.

Roger had come up for a chat and a coffee, and to cadge a cigarette. He was tall for the bridge, and stooped as he moved from the kettle to the chart table, glancing his eyes over our course and impatiently pacing before the console. He looked shiftily out of the corner of one eye in one of his frequent attempts to seem sly, but instead he looked comic. He could have been playing the part of the wicked uncle in an amateur dramatic society pantomime, and I thought him harmless.

Billy was on Forenoon watch. With Keith off-duty recovering from malaria, Afternoon watch was being split between Billy and the First, so they were both working two six-hour shifts with only six hours' break in between. The Mexican cadets Ramiro and Jesus also helped out, recording the ship's performance in the Deck Log in broken English.

Billy was pacing the length of the bridge and swaying his chart pencil about like a baton. He stopped suddenly, put the end of his pencil between his lips and twisted it slowly round and round. Then he began to pace up and down again.

Roger slouched about and attempted to interest the Third in conversation, but Billy was either conducting his invisible orchestra or drilling a hole from his mouth through to the back of his head, and ignored the Chief Engineer. Billy had sat for his Master's Certificate on his last shore leave and the results were already four days overdue. He had hoped they would be waiting for him with the agent in Monrovia. Now they would come through Doug in the radio room, as all important messages did, and be halfway around the ship before he heard them himself.

Billy already held a First Class Deck Certificate, which technically entitled him to serve as First Mate, but, with so few ships working, the prospects for promotion were slight. A Fourth needed a Second Class Certificate, which should have enabled him to serve as Second Mate. A Third needed to hold the qualifications of a Shipmaster. If Billy passed, there would be three fully qualified captains on our vessel (the Mate also held his Master's ticket), although only the Old Man (who was an Extra Master Mariner) had ever held command. It would probably be another twenty years before Billy was in charge of his own ship, if ever. The shipping line was renowned as a 'dead man's shoes company'.

'Began putting in hours for my steerage a few years back,' said Roger, wallowing up and down before the wheel with his hands in his pockets.

'Soon gave it up. Bor-ring,' and he mimicked a yawn. 'Never see anything but sea.'

He put down his coffee cup, lit up one of Billy's cigarettes, and scurried back down to the engine room like an overgrown rat.

When I came on board, the officers had appeared very practical men. The engineers talked about how to fix the pistons and the deck officers calculated our course on a chart. They all ate enormously, drank with a terrific thirst, and publicly scoffed at finer feelings.

It had taken a while for me to realise that I was sailing with a boatload of romantics.

When Billy took over from Keith on the bridge, the 1230 message grew from a thirty-second announcement to five minutes of assorted oddments of information. Our position, speed and Estimated Time of Arrival were supplemented by the movements of the stars or possible sightings of planets. Soon messages were relayed at other times of the day if something important was noted from the bridge, such as a school of dolphins or the fin of a shark, or if we were sailing through an area with particularly interesting geographical features. Although the sea might spread out in a silvery blanket for days on end, below the surface the scenery changed dramatically. Billy described the huge mountain ranges and frightening precipices. Admiralty charts portray the earth far more accurately than any other sort of map. On a chart, countries appear as flat, featureless, buff-coloured areas, but the ocean floor is littered with symbols and warnings.

Two days out of Monrovia, we would clip the edge of the Romanche Trench, a deep underwater valley hundreds of miles long, greater than anything on earth. The Romanche Trench, Billy explained, breaks the underwater mountain range called the Atlantic Ridge, which stretches from Iceland to the tip of Africa. For almost its entire ten thousand mile length, its summits are submerged beneath at least a mile of water. Only the very highest peaks break through the surface, and these are called Gough, Bouvet, and Tristan da Cunha.

At dinner Billy came over the tannoy to say that a single dolphin was following us on the starboard quarter, which was a rare sight. Dolphins usually travel in schools. One by one the officers left the mess, mumbling, 'have to write up some notes before going on' or, 'need some kip'. I left my Eskimo Nell and hurried out on deck. The officers were dotted along the starboard rail, laughing quietly to themselves at the antics of the lone dolphin, leaping high out of the water and grinning broadly.

Despite the early start, the four to eight watch, catching sunrise and sunset, was the most popular. 'They're beautiful sometimes, you know,' Billy had said, the poet's voice trying to break out through his Irish brogue. The First Mate, whose watch it was, was considered lucky. Other officers often found an excuse to come on to the bridge – to cadge a cigarette, have a cup of coffee, check if there was any work the Mate needed done – but they really came up to watch the sunset. Sometimes several men would be hanging around at the back of the bridge, boiling the same kettle of water over and over again until the sun went down and the bridge was dark, apart from the lights on the dials.

The seamen had already jolted me out of the cosy portraits I had of them, formed by landsmen's ideas of what seafarers are supposed to be like.

'It's the Mate you'll have to look out for,' the incoming Second Secretary had informed me at the Irish Embassy in Lagos. 'Mates work by the rule book. They're always looking over their shoulder for that thing or person that could get in the way of them gaining command.'

I had read in a book, 'The engineers on merchant vessels are most easy-going, as their job is considerably less stressful than working the bridge.'

'The Chief Steward will be queer,' Simon Plunkett had told me in the agent's office at Apapa. 'They always are.'

Only the Old Man resembled the landsman's portrait of a seaman of his rank. Masters of merchant vessels are believed to fall into two types – the jolly, genial type, and the stern, silent type – and the Captain fitted squarely into the latter category.

Our Captain had held the lonely rank of master for over ten years, having gained his first command aged forty, nearly twenty years after he had passed his master's ticket. Before he had been promoted to the boat deck and retired to the captain's quarters, he must have drunk in the officers' saloon, joined in the jokes and swapped yarns. It was impossible to imagine our Captain, as staunch as a Free Kirk elder, joining in the social life of the ship. Though whether he had always been so dour, or whether he had cultivated humourlessness on assuming command, none of his men, except Jimmy, were old enough to know.

The Captain had never married, and lived with his sister Margaret in a cottage in Aberdeenshire. He owned a small dinghy, and spent most of his leave sailing in the bay by Dunnottar Castle. An old man in the village kept the hull salted while he was at sea.

'I like taking her out,' he said one breakfast in a rare use of the first-person pronoun. 'No log books, nothing like that. I can really relax.'

His one regret was that he had never commanded a vessel round Cape Horn.

'Perhaps next voyage,' he said cheerily. 'Could be chartered out. Never know.'

The following breakfast he elaborated upon his ambition:

'Icebergs. Icebergs are the main problem.'

Then two days later:

'Perhaps, in retirement, given the right boat, I'll sail solo round the world. Yes. Solo.'

It was fit for the Captain to keep his distance. The men respected the Old Man; he was, they said, a 'proper seaman', the highest compliment they could pay. But the loneliness of his position encouraged introspection and broodiness, and captains were known to have peculiar obsessions which festered in the isolation of the boat deck. One former captain was known to play chess with himself in his cabin. He took on the part of both players, jumping from one side of the board to the other, throwing out challenges to his invisible opponent and arguing over procedural matters. He used to remark to his First at breakfast that Player One plotted well last night, but Player Two needed to brush up on the use of his queen. Another captain was fanatical about ironing. (Now even captains have to iron their own uniforms.) He was a real stickler for creases, and used to comment if he spotted any wrinkles in a subordinate's uniform, offering to iron them out himself.

With our Old Man, it was murders and mechanical navigation aids.

When economic and military might depended upon control of the oceans, governments sponsored research into methods of accurately calculating a ship's position at sea. In 1714, the British Parliament, on the recommendation of Sir Isaac Newton, had passed an Act establishing the Commissioners for the Discovery of Longitude at Sea. This committee of distinguished men was charged with the responsibility of awarding twenty thousand pounds to the first person who invented a means of calculating longitude.

It was recognised that there was a pressing need for such a discovery to be made. As long as trade had been confined to coastal waters or areas with well-charted islands, bearings could be taken from land. But by the early eighteenth century, France and England were fiercely competing in the vast North Atlantic for the North American trade. The key to colonial victory was control of the lines of communication, which meant having fast, reliable shipping routes.

A ship's latitude could be calculated easily; the most simple method was by measuring the height of the Pole or North Star in degrees above the horizon. This measurement, duly corrected, gave the observer's latitude. Astronomers soon compiled tables of other stars, including the sun, from which latitude could be calculated. But finding the longitude was far more difficult, as the earth spins around on a North–South axis so a star's altitude has no direct relationship to an observer's longitudinal position. Without knowing how to calculate longitude, a ship had to 'run down her latitude', sailing north or south until she reached the latitude of her goal, then heading east or west until she stumbled across her destination. It was a haphazard and unreliable method of crossing the ocean, and, if only longitude could be calculated accurately, a ship's voyage would be considerably shortened by enabling her to chart a direct course.

It was known that the longitude of any place on the globe was proportional to the time the earth took to rotate on its axis between that place and the meridian at Greenwich. The earth takes twenty-four hours to rotate three hundred and sixty degrees. Therefore one hour time difference is equivalent to fifteen degrees (one twenty-fourth of three hundred and sixty) east or west of the meridian. If local noon occurred one hour later than the noon at Greenwich, then the longitude of that place would be fifteen degrees west. The Commissioners realised that a method was needed that could be relied upon to carry the time at the Greenwich meridian about the globe, unaffected by temperature and conditions at sea. With the time at Greenwich and the time locally both known, it would be possible to calculate a ship's longitude.

Many extraordinary schemes were put before the Board. Two scholarly clergymen presented a method by which lightships would be moored in specific locations along the North Atlantic trade routes. At midnight, the lightships would fire a shell to the height of 6,440 feet. The clergymen calculated that these midnight explosions would be heard and seen up to eighty-five miles away, and thereby provide a means by which a ship's clock could be checked and corrected.

While academics at Oxford, Cambridge and London devoted their research to methods of calculating longitude, hundreds of miles away in Barrow-on-Humber a carpenter called John Harrison set out to construct a clock which he hoped would win him the twenty thousand pound prize. Harrison was entirely self-taught, yet he had already constructed a number of remarkable timepieces. The conditions under which a clock had to maintain its accuracy on a long sea voyage, however, presented a particular problem – there would be extreme changes in climate, and the rolling and pitching of the ship must be taken into account. Harrison's first attempt was a massive structure weighing seventy-two pounds, with all the wheels carved from wood. By his fourth, his 'sea-clock' had been reduced to little more than the size of a gentleman's pocket watch, and was constructed of metal. The Commissioners had stipulated that the winning timepiece must not lose or gain more than one and a half seconds a day. Harrison put his sea-clock to trial on a 156-day voyage to the West Indies and home, during which it lost only fifteen seconds. He was entitled to the twenty thousand pound prize. But the learned Commissioners were suspicious of the carpenter from Barrow, and demanded that he construct another clock, as accurate, to prove that this was not a one-off chance achievement, and that his timepiece could be copied and put into general use.

Harrison, after over forty years' research and by then in his seventies, grew embittered at the Board's continual application of additional criteria to be met before he could claim the prize. When he was asked to hand over his sea-clock to them for yet more controlled trials, he suspected some of the Commissioners might try and copy it or, even worse, sell its secrets to the French. Harrison's final few years were consumed in a long struggle to obtain the recognition and award due to him.

At the same time as Harrison was working on his timepiece, an astronomer in East Barnet called John Hadley was searching for a method of finding longitude by measuring the angle between the moon and sun or a star. He had engineered a quadrant made of mahogany which measured angles by reflection, presenting it before the Royal Society in January 1721. The Society's *Record* noted that Hadley 'shewed the Society his apparatus for managing his reflecting telescope, which was highly approved of both for its simplicity and for the ease and certainty wherewith it performs the notions requisite to follow the heavens'.

Hadley's invention was refined into the first sextant, manufactured in 1757. John 'Longitude' Harrison's sea-clock was the model for the chronometer. Thanks to the endeavours of a carpenter from Barrow-on-Humber and an astronomer from East Barnet, British vessels were able to plot their course accurately across the great ocean. By 1760, Britain had won control of the North Atlantic trade route.

Billy had said he would teach me how to use the sextant. The company's Bridge Order Book, known as the Bible, required a master to ensure that the position of his ship was verified as often as possible by terrestrial, celestial or other methods, with particular attention paid to the noon sight.

When I had asked how the noon sight was taken, the seamen had responded by telling me how it *used* to be taken, many years before. This tendency to reply to my questions as if they had been put at least twenty years earlier was confusing at first; I could not understand why a number of things on the *Minos* were not as I had been led to expect. Where were the passengers who slept under canvas on deck? Why did the *Minos* have metal rather than scrubbed wooden decks? And why was there no Chinese laundry-man or Kruboy whose job it was to wash my clothes?

When I asked about the noon sight I was told that the Captain, the First Mate, the Second Mate, the Third Mate, the Fourth Mate, the Fifth Mate and a cadet would be standing on the bridge wing at midday holding their sextants. The Captain would say, 'Well, what do you get?', and the Second would shout out, 'Nine degrees, thirty-two minutes North, sir.' The other officers would grunt confirmation, 'It's about there,' and the Captain would announce, 'We'll make it nine degrees, thirty-two minutes North.' Then the officers would consult the correction tables and leaf through the *Nautical Almanac* on the bridge, and latitude would be calculated. Once their sums agreed, this position would be entered in the Deck Log.

So when there was just the Captain and Billy on the bridge at

midday, I wondered what was wrong. I knew Keith was sick, but
where were the rest of them? When I asked Billy, he said the Second
sometimes joined in, if he was out from lunch in time.

Satellite navigation systems provide extremely accurate positions. In addition to a Marconi satellite system, the *Minos*'s bridge
was fitted with a Decca Navigator which, by reflecting radio waves
from a chain of transmitters and plotting their intersection, could
pinpoint our position within a quarter of a nautical mile. But the
noon sight on the *Minos* was taken with a sextant. The Old Man
insisted upon it.

Billy took me outside on to the bridge wing and handed me the
heavy metal object. Through the small telescope attached to the
frame, I brought the darkly shaded sun down until its lower limb
bounced on the horizon. A sextant in perfect adjustment has an
accuracy of better than half a minute. The Captain, who had been
at sea nearly half a century, admired Billy's skill with the
instrument and encouraged his reliance on mechanical aids. Billy
in turn enjoyed tutoring me in a navigational system that was
decades out of date. By the end of the week I could take shots with a
sextant but still couldn't confidently read the analogue on the
Electronic Speed Log or decipher the Weather Fax.

All through the first full day at sea the *Minos* buzzed with chatter
about the continent we had just left. In the bar that night, the talk
was of Africa too. For weeks we had been tied up along the West
African coast; none of the officers had ventured more than a mile
away from port, and only a few had bothered to go ashore. After
dinner, we had talked about the old days, the weather, the Old
Man, but never Africa. With Africa safely over the horizon, it
became our main topic of conversation.

'Ever seen the Congo?' asked Doug.

'Why do you like the West Coast, then?' Billy mumbled, worried
that someone else might hear.

'Ever been with a black man?' whispered Roger so close that the
inside of my ear steamed up.

'Did I ever tell you the President of Liberia – Will Tubman was his
name – awarded me the Star of Africa?' said Jimmy.

After weeks on the ship, there were still some officers whose
names I did not know. The 'Lecky', a lanky blond from Liverpool,

and the swarthy Third Engineer drank together in the bar and kept to themselves. A ship's people, even if just two dozen, was like a population of hundreds ashore, and I would only ever speak to a few of them. At first this seemed strange, but soon I found it quite natural that someone who quartered one deck down from me and worked several decks below that, was as far away as someone who lived on the other side of a large city, and it was hardly surprising that we rarely met, and then only exchanged a curt nod, as distant neighbours might.

Steve had just arrived from the engine room for his first pint. He was still in his boilersuit and his handsome face shone with oil and sweat.

Roger winked at me with the whole side of his face so his clipped beard looked like a furry animal crawling up his cheek.

'Did. You. Ever?' he mouthed silently, distorting his lips into the shape of each word.

I ignored him, which was a mistake.

'Hey!' he shouted across the cavernous saloon. 'I SAID DID YOU EVER DO IT WITH A BLACK MAN?'

The burr of the engines rose up from below and vibrated the orange vinyl partitions. Steve's handsome glistening face fixed on me.

Roger was waiting for his answer. No one spoke.

There was the sharp pop of a ring being pulled.

'Another beer, Doug?' shouted Jimmy from the bar.

Roger dropped his stare, turned towards the First Mate and began to chat loudly about when he was last on the Coast and this big black mammy, the size of Jimmy, had offered him her body in exchange for a fire extinguisher. Even Roger was talking about Africa.

I went up to the bridge before turning in, to say goodnight to Billy. He was hunched over the chart table, his solid body illuminated from the neck down by the light above the charts.

'Want to try the sextant on the stars at dawn?' he smiled.

'No, another time.'

The phone rang. It was the Captain to tell us he had just heard on the BBC World Service that a man with a shot gun had run amok and killed four shoppers in a While-U-Wait Heel and Key Bar. Five more had been taken to hospital. Billy asked which town. The

Captain couldn't remember, but one of the injured was in a critical condition. He predicted the death toll would be up to half a dozen by the end of the night.

Pulling off my boilersuit and sliding naked into bed, I could hear the fanfare of the BBC World Service seeping through the partition between the Old Man's quarters and my cabin.

> This is London.
> *Beep. Beep. Beep. Beeeeeeep.*
> Midnight, Greenwich Mean Time, BBC World Service.
> The news read by Liz Francis.
> Afghan rebels have attacked the military stronghold of . . .

I looked at my clock. Half past ten. Probably not the time on any solid piece of land. Just ship's time.

Within minutes the Captain and I would be rocked to sleep in the safe cradle of the sea.

Chapter Ten

We were now well out to sea, but the further away we sailed from Africa, the more we talked about her.

'I'm a legend in Freetown, you know. A legend,' bragged Jimmy after breakfast. 'I'm known everywhere there. When I arrive they shout all along the street:

> PAT-TER-SON, PAT-TER-SON
> PATTY, PATTY, PATTY
> PAT-TER-SON.'

He arranged rows of frozen sausage rolls on a baking tray as he sang.

Chief Cook George was listening to Jimmy's stories with a wry smile. He bent over the large saucepan of pepper soup, broke the thin orange film of palm oil floating on top with a ladle, and dipped slowly up and down. His hair was beginning to grey at the ends, as if Jimmy had taken the flourshaker and sprinkled it over his Chief Cook's wiry black curls. George's head rocked from side to side as he stirred, and his lips moved slightly, muttering silently to himself as old men do. He could have been incanting a spell over a cauldron.

Jimmy and George had served together with the shipping line on and off for twenty-seven years. Jimmy knew George's home was in Freetown, but there was no one else for Jimmy to tell tales of the Coast, so he continued to speak to his old cook as if he were a cadet fresh from Liverpool. Until, that is, I had arrived and provided him with another audience.

Jimmy interrupted a list he was making out loud of all the important people in Freetown who were his personal friends when he noticed me standing in the doorway.

'I've worked with these lads for years now. I know their families,' he said affectionately, waving a hand in the direction of George, who continued to slowly dip his ladle. The cook acknowledged his change of role from audience to subject of Jimmy's tale with a slight widening of his smile.

I was beginning to understand that Jimmy, like many of the officers, didn't hate Africans at all. He only hated the fact that he liked them. He was, after all, a British officer and ought to know better.

Jimmy tugged at the front of his shirt, tucking it fiercely into the top of his tropical shorts, and tapped the three gold bands on his epaulettes with his index finger, reminding himself who and what he was by the touch of his Merchant Navy uniform.

'Effing Africans,' he spat, stubbing out his cigarette violently on the steel surface. 'Nignogs. Do you know what we call Nigerian Shipping Lines?'

Of course I knew. He had told me many times already. Niggernash.

'Niggernash,' he chuckled. 'Effing Niggernash! I'll go and find Sparky. More appreciative bloody audience than this lot.'

It was a barroom joke that Jimmy now spent more time in the radio room than in the galley, waiting on the reply to his application for voluntary redundancy. Jimmy, apparently believing Doug could conjure up the response from Liverpool on his machines and not merely relay it, plied him with favours. The stocky Radio Officer was treated to extra large helpings at dinner followed by double rums in the officers' saloon.

Doug grew no fatter but considerably more morose. Under the influence of Jimmy's free drinks, he confessed before a crowd that his only sister was 'Nervous. Nervous in the head,' and his twin teenage daughters were 'No good'. I also learnt that he harboured a dream to canoe up the Congo River.

After one night when Jimmy had been particularly hospitable, Doug pulled me to a corner of the saloon and confided his plan. Did I have experience of canoeing long distances? What did I think he would need to take? Did I think it was a good idea? When should he go? Could I help him?

'I just want to get in a canoe and disappear,' he whispered, screwing up his face as if in pain. 'Right *into* it. I want to disappear right *into* it.'

I rummaged for information on the river in my African guidebooks and spent an hour in the ship's library hunting for references. The ship's library was an eclectic collection of books chosen by the librarian of the Marine Society in London, mostly consisting of hardback fiction with the guarantee that 'nothing obscene, obscure or currently controversial' was included. The books were changed at the end of each four-month voyage for a fresh stock. The Marine Society charged the shipping line a modest fee for this service, which the Society believed was well worth the immeasurable benefits. 'The modern seafarer is generally well-educated and as a result is often interested in self improvement. Seafarers' Libraries offer the means of achieving this at sea,' advertised the Society. 'The absence of such a facility can be frustrating and this in time leads to a less than efficient seafarer. Not all seafarers watch video and TV, few can occupy their leisure hours at sea with physical exercise alone, and the bar as a leisure pursuit can be particularly counter-productive to the usefulness of a seafarer. Books are the flexible answer to the five-minute break or the full watch below, taking the mind off the work and relieving boredom. A refreshed mind is better able to cope with the work to be done.'

The Marine Society's hand-picked selection was supplemented by castoffs from earlier members of crew – mainly popular novels of heroic deeds at sea – and the odd donation from a charity which still considered sailors worthy recipients of benevolence. The collection offered a researcher bizarre and disjointed glimpses into their subject. I found a book called *In Lionland* which included great quotes from Henry Morton Stanley's *Through the Dark Continent*. In 1877, Stanley had been the first white man to battle along the entire length of the Congo, from the clear emerald stream bubbling in the heart of Africa to the heavy, silty water entering the Atlantic Ocean three thousand miles later.

H.M. Stanley and Wales was probably the gift of a baptist mission. Insisting on using Stanley's birthname of John Rowlands, which the explorer himself had disowned through shame at his illegitimacy, the tired pamphlet portrayed the trans-African explorer as a dutiful son whose first appointment on returning from Abyssinia was to take tea with his elderly Aunt Mary. 'He corresponded with his mother and many members of his family, bringing them gifts and mementoes,' it read. 'He was by no means forgetful of his homeland and family background, and the time is long overdue to give him the recognition he deserves as one of Wales' most eminent sons.' *Portugal in Africa* told the story of fifteenth-century Portuguese adventurer Diego Cao, who, forty miles off the West African coast, bent over the side of his boat, tasted the water, and found it sweet. Following the swirls of muddied water, he sailed into the gaping mouth of the Congo and erected a stone cross claiming this broad highway into the interior for his king. It was the most powerful river any white man had ever seen.

I traced the great arc of the Congo in the old atlas. From the sea at Boma, the river reached in a mighty curve eight hundred miles north to Lisala before tumbling back south to Kisangani, crossing the equator twice.

I consulted the *Africa Pilot*, which broke from its technical vocabulary to call the Congo 'this noble river'. The currents are strong, and papyrus and water hyacinths torn away from the banks cluster into floating islands over half a cable long. At its widest, the river measures ten miles across, like an inland sea. The Bakongo, who lent their name to the river, call the angry flow *Nzere* – the river that swallows all rivers.

The Congo River lives up to its century-old reputation as the supreme test of manliness. In the upper reaches, there are still hippopotami and crocodiles, and pygmies live in scattered villages along the banks. Closer to the sea, mangrove swamps are broken by towns called Mosquito Creek, Fetish Wood, Banana Town, Pirate Creek, and whirlpools named the Cauldron of Hell where canoeists have to be careful not to get tangled in a telephone line which has been strung across the basin of violent water. On the Point of Dry Thicket, on the southern bank at the mouth of the river, Diego Cao's marble cross stands five yards high.

I turned to the *Pilot* for practical answers to Doug's queries. When should he go? The *Pilot* advised:

During the wet season the climate is not particularly healthy,

but during the dry season, May to October, it is not unhealthy.
A doctor is available for urgent cases only.

The *Pilot*, like the school atlas, listed Port Malebo as Stanley Pool,
Boyoma Falls as Stanley Falls and Kisangani as Stanleyville. It did
not record that the river itself was renamed Fleuve Zaire in 1971, as
part of the Party of the Congolese Workers' 'Authenticity Programme'. The *Pilot* judged, as it did with almost every West African
entry, that there were no reliable charts.

Would it be possible to paddle up from the river's mouth at Boma,
over the rapids and cataracts? Or should Doug attempt a down-river
journey from Kisangani? Following this seaward route, Stanley and
his one-hundred-strong expedition had covered the first one
thousand four hundred miles in four months. But less than three
hundred miles from the ocean, they had met the rapids:

> We are past Mbelo Falls, and a stream, brown-black and
> menacing, enters the main river from behind the rock islets; we
> are whirled round twice by the eddying pool, precipitated into
> a dancing, seething, hissing cauldron, just as if the river was
> boiling over . . . and away down stream we dart, racing amid
> noise and waves and foam, when the cold grey cliffs drop sheer
> down, and finally emerge in Nguru basin, borne on a slackened
> current; and it is then we sigh, and murmur, 'Saved again!'

The perpetual clamour of the rapids destroyed Stanley's nerves and
sent his henchman mad. Stanley recorded in his diary, 'We have a
horror of the river.'

It seemed Doug would have to circumvent this difficult stretch by
trekking overland through the hills or riding on the railroad built by
the Belgians early this century, rejoining the river at its lower
reaches near Matadi. From here he would only have to paddle
eighty miles to the sea.

I drew up a list of questions for Doug. Could he handle a pirogue?
Did he speak French? Did he think he could eat smoked monkey if
pushed? Could I come too? It would be our shared secret on board,
our African Adventure. I scribbled another question in the margin –
*Why do I find it easier to imagine myself in a canoe on the Congo
than a British merchant vessel in the North Atlantic?* – then wound
spirals all over it so it looked like a doodle.

I made a special note that Stanley was five feet five inches tall, about the same height as Doug. In an attempt to better himself, the Victorian explorer had run away to sea, aged seventeen, to be a deckhand on a merchant vessel.

I took my books and notes to lunch the next day. Doug waved the small pile away from him as if infected, muttering 'romantic toss' with a mouth full of Crumbed Cod.

Later that day, bumping into him on my way past the radio room to the bridge for Dogs, Doug lifted his glasses, tweaked his nose with his thumb and forefinger, and replaced his glasses at a slight tilt.

'About the other night, in the bar,' he said, looking at the floor. 'Bit carried away. The drink. Talked nonsense.'

He slid his toes together and apart as if practising ballet positions.

'OK?'

'OK,' I said.

Canoeing up the Congo was never mentioned again.

The *Minos* was like a country, with distinct peoples and its own climate. We were airconditioned, so even docked at Douala, where it had been unbearably muggy ashore with the temperature in the mid-nineties, we were cool inside our cabins. At sea, the airtight doors kept out any hint of a breeze. It was never force five but only 'light airs' within the ship.

The only air in my cabin came from the circular air-conditioning vent in the centre of the ceiling. In Africa, I had been used to sleeping outside, and the chill in the cabin at night and the weight of the bedclothes I used to keep me warm had disturbed my sleep. By the end of the first week I had stuffed one of the ship's towels into the vent. It stopped the cold air coming through, and I slept more comfortably. But, with no ventilation, soon my cabin began to smell, and the horse bridle in the back of my cupboard made its presence known. I didn't mind at all; I liked the fetidness of it. It reminded me of the cloying harmattan air.

The *Minos* even had its own language, which I was just beginning to learn. On my third day on board I had asked for the swimming pool.

'Abaft the funnel,' had been the reply, and I waited until the seaman had turned the corner before descending into the nearest stairwell, not knowing which direction was abaft or where the funnel would be.

The language of the *Minos* did not only contain new terms and phrases. Far more confusingly, the ship's language used old words that I was familiar with, but gave them totally different meanings. 'Floors' were, I was told, not the surfaces you walk on but transverse *vertical* plates in the ship's frame. A mile at sea was not the same as a mile on land, but considerably longer. That was not too difficult to fathom. But at anchor in Suellaba Bay, I had asked if Keith was going to leave the ship in Douala.

'Leave the ship? Why should I leave the ship?'

'To see the town,' I offered cautiously.

'To see the town? I might run ashore, but I doubt it. Nothing worth seeing these days.'

'Leaving the ship', I learnt to the seamen's glee in the bar, was what happened at the end of a voyage. When visiting a port of call, you were 'going ashore'.

I had been confusing more than mere phrases. Although the men occasionally spent an evening on land, the ship was never more than a mile away with her gangway down and deck lights blazing. Only at the voyage end, when the officers drove away to their brick houses, did they leave her.

I soon devised a method of teaching myself the ship's language which reduced the chance of being laughed at or made to look a fool. Every morning I opened at random my *Companion to Ships and the Sea* and learnt a new phrase. The dictionary could be used like a Berlitz phrasebook, and I discreetly referred to it out of sight of the natives so as not to appear ignorant. I learnt that ropes are only hauled, never pulled; ceilings were called deckheads; ladders were called companionways; and floors, of course, were always called decks.

I had also heard one of the seamen describe a small lifeboat on a rough sea and her 'burthen'. Later, in the privacy of my cabin, I looked up this new word. The dictionary explained burthen was:

The older term used to express a ship's tonnage or carrying capacity. It was based on the number of tuns of wine that a ship could carry in her holds, the total number giving her

burthen. The term remained as an expression of a ship's size
until the end of the eighteenth century and gradually fell into
disuse.

Often I looked up a term which I had overheard in the bar, only to
find the dictionary said it was last used over two hundred years ago.

The seaman's country was smaller than any state on land. But
although the *Minos* was only five hundred feet from bow to stern,
with a beam of eighty feet, there were whole areas I had not
explored. The Captain and I were the only inhabitants of the boat
deck, just below the bridge, which we shared with the ship's
library. The boat deck was a quiet, bookish region, where the
Captain and I led isolated lives and had few visitors.

The route from my cabin to the mess and bar on the poop took
me through the upper and lower bridge decks by the internal
companionways. On the upper bridge deck, the officers lived in
their single cabins and conducted their social life behind the
closed doors of their quarters, inviting each other in for a drink, or
socialised in the bar. On the lower bridge deck, the Kru slept two
to a room. As I passed down through the decks, I could hear the
heavy beat of West African music vibrating the partitions and the
sound of voices shouting along the alleyways, 'Hey, brother – how
now?'

Once, I had leant through the doorway into the lower bridge deck
alleyway and saw men squatting on the linoleum, or sitting with
their legs out straight in front of them, blocking the path. Some
were playing cards, others just chatting or taking a nap. It was like
an impossibly narrow underground African street.

The lower bridge deck was out of bounds, considered almost a
no-go area by the officers. It was tacitly agreed that junior officers
and crew were not to trespass on the elevated boat deck, where the
Old Man and I lived. Only on the poop, housing the saloon, messes
and galley, was everyone on board allowed to be on the same
level. The poop deck was lorded over by Jimmy.

It wasn't until three days out of Monrovia that I discovered
Jimmy's realm expanded beyond the poop. After a luncheon of
Lamb Chops Milanese, Creamed Spinach and Boiled and Baked
Potatoes, Jimmy invited me to descend into the deck below and
tour his walk-in larders and cold stores.

The giant steel doors lined each side of the alleyway like body storage compartments in a morgue. Jimmy creaked them open to reveal magnificent steamy interiors filled with sides of ham, whole truckles of hard cheeses, giant packs of pink sausages and bacon, long-life milk stored in plastic bags with taps on them like udders, and sacks of pepper for the crew's soup. The colder the box, the more gruesome the contents, until the steamiest was filled with nothing but great carcasses of flesh.

The shipping line fed its men generously – I had already put on weight with the thrice-daily meals. But compared to the rations allotted each seaman a hundred years earlier, the portions were modest. Then, the daily allowance for each officer had been one pound of bread (if the ship had a bakery) or Captain's Biscuit (a hard cake of flour and water, and favourite nibble of the seaborne black-headed weevil); one and a half pounds of salted meat; and a sufficient supply of potatoes or yams. For breakfast, each seaman received an additional half pound of pickled pork, beef or bacon. He was allowed one pound of sugar and butter, plus half a pound of cheese per week. Plum puddings were served on Sundays.

Despite these enormous helpings, many seamen suffered from a diet which, after the first week at sea, contained no fresh fruit or vegetables. Scurvy, caused by a deficiency of vitamin C, killed more seamen than battles and founderings combined. In 1753 Dr James Lind in his *Treatise of the Scurvy* had shown that citrus fruit were an effective cure, and by the end of the century lemon juice was compulsory issue in the Royal Navy. By the nineteenth century, limes were more abundant and cheaper than lemons, so lime juice replaced the old rations and scurvy re-emerged: limes contain only half the vitamin C of lemons. It wasn't until vitamins were discovered in 1912 that scurvy was brought under control.

In addition to an unbalanced diet, a seaman's stomach fell prey to unscrupulous pursers who were paid with a small direct salary supplemented by a commission on the daily victualling allowance. While the purser drew the allowances from the store at the full rate of sixteen ounces to the pound, he issued supplies at fourteen ounces to the pound, making a commission in kind of twelve and a half per cent. This system was easily open to abuse, and many pursers retired very rich men.

'Have to stock up well. That's part of the job – knowing what you'll need. Can't exactly pop out to the local supermarket.' Jimmy nodded through the door of a walk-in larder at half a dozen crates of mangoes piled up as high as me. 'Picked them up in Tema. Saving them for later in the voyage, when the other fruit runs out.'

The officers often talked of how good a catering officer Jimmy was. They had known bad ones, and would reel off stories of being underfed by men who fiddled the books and pocketed a good portion of the catering budget themselves. They recalled menus so repetitive they didn't know whether it was Tuesday luncheon or Sunday dinner, and meals served so cold the grease shone over them like a varnish.

Jimmy's meals were large, well-cooked and varied.

BOODLES OODLES FOODLE
YORK HAM AND CAULIFLOWER NATURAL
RASPBERRY MOUSSE.

WELSH RAREBIT
GOULASH
ANDERSON'S ARCTIC WONDER.

POTAGE DE APAPA
KIDNEY FRICASSEE
STRAWBERRY CHEESECAKE.

STUFFED PEPPER AFRICAINE
BAKED BOSUN'S SPECIAL
ATLANTIC ICE.

Although his ingredients were limited to the stores in the steamy freezers, Jimmy cooked them in such wild combinations and dubbed his dishes with such cryptic names that every meal was like a TV quiz show in which the officers were all contestants.

'What's Captain's Caper?' the First Mate John asked Abu as he waited at table.

'Don't know, master.'

'I'll have it, anyway,' said John, as if taking up a dare. 'With mashed.'

While waiting for the dish to arrive wagers were put in from pancakes to Scotch Egg in curry sauce, in reference to the Old Man's Aberdonian origins.

I bet it was something to do with fish, perhaps in capers.

Abu ceremoniously deposited a large pie, shaped like an up-turned basin, in front of the First Mate.

The crust gave no clue to its interior. Another round of the game had to be entered before a winner could be announced. John took a hesitant bite.

'Fish,' he said.

I beamed, claiming victory.

'Perhaps meat,' he went on, taking a second, smaller bite.

'Perhaps both?' he added, turning wide-eyed to Abu for clues.

Those of us who had not yet ordered went for the safety of the regular daily alternative – Cold Cuts.

Every morning Jimmy composed the luncheon and dinner menus on a tinny Olivetti typewriter in the purser's office with the relish of a poet. The typed white cards, with the logo of an anchor and our daily position at the top, were propped up on the white linen tablecloths before each meal. We could have reached across and picked up a card, but never did. As we each sat down at table, a steward plucked a menu from between the silver-plated cruets and held it up for our inspection with a muttered 'Master'. It was one of those small formalities on board that had at first made me want to giggle. I soon learnt that these gestures were taken very seriously indeed. Already luncheon was self-service.

'They introduced this self-service lark about a year ago,' said the Captain to me one luncheon over his bowl. 'Before that, every meal was served, like in the evenings now.'

At least at dinner the men were served as befitted officers of the British Mercantile Marine.

It was Sunday, and the luncheon menu was headed 'At Sea. Pub Lunch'.

Sundays on board were much like every other day. The men worked their watches on the bridge or down in the engine room. I was to relieve Sissay on the wheel for Dogs at 1600 hours. We chundered along at twelve and a half knots. We crossed fifteen degrees North making almost due north, and by lunchtime the Mauritanian coast was to the east of us and the northernmost islands of Cape Verde to the west. We all knew it was Sunday and therefore special, however, because of pub lunch.

'It's pub lunch tomorrow,' Roger had said importantly in the bar the night before.

'Pub lunch!' Doug had cheered over a hearty breakfast that morning. The Captain continued to spoon his porridge from the bowl into his puckered mouth. Pub lunch was in the officers' bar, which he never entered. The Captain would be taking luncheon in his cabin.

At lunchtime the saloon filled up a little earlier than usual, and a dart board was taken out from under the video cabinet and hung at the opposite end to the bar. We trotted through into the mess. The typed menu lying on top of the serve-yourself counter read:

CAULIFLOWER CHEESE – SAUSAGE ROLLS – STEAK 'N
KIDNEY PIE
PIZZA – BURGERS – CHIPS – BAKED BEANS.

We helped ourselves to the sausage rolls, pies and burgers shimmering under the heat lamps, and carried our plates back through to the saloon. We ate by balancing them on our laps.

'Hee, hee,' giggled Roger, picking a bit of flaky pastry from his beard. 'It's grand.'

Without having to eat so awkwardly and the slight sense of festivity amongst the men, I would not have known it was Sunday. Perhaps it wasn't. Perhaps we were victim to one of Jimmy's practical jokes. Or perhaps the Chief Steward, lost in a poetic flourish, had accidentally tapped out 'Pub Lunch' at the top of the menu that morning. Only pub lunch separated the endless succession of days at sea into the week we were all familiar with at home. Otherwise the regular periods of daylight and darkness would be distinguishable only, as I wrote in my log, as Day 1, Day 2, Day 3 . . .

I carried my plate, smeared with brown sauce, back through to the galley. I hadn't been on deck all day and could have been staying in the worn grandeur of the Adelphi Hotel, Liverpool. Perhaps Sarah was right; the *Minos* was just like a great big floating British hotel.

'Enjoy your pub lunch?' beamed Jimmy, overseeing the washing up. 'Mind you, it's not like the old days, when all the lads used to come down. Especially with a woman on board . . .'

He was in a good mood, and looking for a rile.

'Is today *really* Sunday?' I asked.

'Of course it's bloody Sunday. You had pub lunch, didn't you? If
it's pub lunch, it's Sunday.'

There was no arguing with Jimmy's logic.

I decided it was time to go on deck.

On deck all likeness to the Adelphi vanished. The temperature
was in the mid-seventies and a light wind blew with a low swell,
rocking the ship from bow to stern. I was startled to discover that I
was at sea and moving.

I spent most of my free time on deck, sitting in my old
deckchair. In the promotional pictures of our sister ships hanging
in the officers' saloon, the decks were always empty, sunny areas
with no one around. These pictures were a shipper's dream. All
research in the shipping industry is concentrated on designing
systems which need fewer and fewer sailors to man them. The
ships in the pictures in the officers' saloon were premonitions of
these ghost-driven vessels. Yet on the *Minos*, there were always
men on deck, painting, on the bridge wing on lookout, hanging
over a deckrail, surveying the containers, or checking the hatches.
Above decks, the deck plating had to be cleaned with an electric-
ally driven chipping hammer to remove the rust where the combination of salt water and sea air had eaten into the metal. The bulk
of the work was around the accommodation block situated aft,
where there were the most rails. The sound of the chipping gang
descaling was like an insistent drill, and on these days I stayed in
my cabin.

The *Minos* was methodically maintained as a matter of pride
rather than necessity. The Greek ships I had seen in port along the
coast had been unashamedly rusting all over. Their hulls were
peeling, their rails were cracked, and they had rotten wooden
gangways which creaked as they were made ready for sea. The
Greeks didn't seem to care what other ships thought of them.

British seamen, however, are known for their fastidiousness.
They like their ships to be smart and crisply painted, uniform grey
and white being the preferred colours. 'Shipshape and Bristol
fashion' originates from when Bristol was Britain's major west
coast port and her ships were renowned for being maintained in
proper good order. Yet the scruffy Greeks worked the oceans as
competently as our line, and would prove to outlive us.

There was a tiny pool abaft the bridge which was filled every morning by the Mate from a giant hydrant (known as a 'stopcock' ashore), and I had got into the habit of having a swim about an hour after lunch, before I relieved Sissay at the wheel for Dogs.

The pool was a ten-foot-square hole cut into the deck, as deep as it was broad. The water was piped up from the sea, and along the coast it had been warm and murky. Out in the ocean, it grew colder day by day. It also became more stormy, as the water in the postage-stamp pool rocked with the ship, echoing the waves below. Sometimes, since we'd set out for the ocean, the waves had slapped over the side on to the deck and the pool had been half emptied, and I had been able to stand on the bottom.

When I dipped my toes into the water about an hour after pub lunch it was very cold. We had passed through the Equatorial Counter Current and were into the deep ocean. I jumped in and hit the surface with a gasp. The ship lurched and a wave threw me to one side of the pool, then dragged me back to the other. The water tasted very salty.

I usually had the pool to myself. Although they spent a lifetime floating about on top of the sea, most of the seamen couldn't swim. Their only contact with the ocean was drinking it. Waste heat from the engines, operating at over four hundred degrees centigrade, was harnessed to produce steam which, passed through an evaporator, distilled the sea into drinking water.

The joviality of pub lunch and the fact that it was, after all, Sunday must have encouraged Steve to take a dip.

He sat on the side of the pool and let his long freckly legs dangle in the water. They went pink from just below his knees, and he smiled over to me, 'Cold!'

'Jump!' I shouted, as he slid in.

I gasped as the waves bounced me backwards and forwards, one landing me on the side like a beached whale. A wave crashed around Steve's head, turning his sandy hair dull brown. My foot kicked the back of his leg; one of his straggling arms clipped my shoulder. As we laughed and spluttered around the cube of water, our bobbing heads emerged a foot apart. I was acutely embarrassed. It was like sharing a bath with someone. Even worse, it was like sharing a bath with Steve, the Fourth Engineer.

The intimacy of swimming together was strong and disturbing. I wanted to leave, but I didn't want Steve to be watching as I pulled my body out of the water and over the side.

The Fourth Engineer hauled himself up out of the pool and ran for his towel.

'Brrrrr,' he shivered. 'Freezing out here. It's warmer where you are. I better come back in.'

He stood still for a moment, his hands resting lightly on his narrow hips, then winked without smiling. I dived back under the crest of a wave, to hide myself in the water.

What did Steve want of me? Why couldn't he just accept me as one of the men?

I waited until he was safely down below before I hoisted myself out and sat on the side, letting the salt blow dry in ashy patches on my skin.

Chapter Eleven

LATITUDE 17°22′ NORTH, LONGITUDE 18°10′ WEST
TO LATITUDE 22°38′ NORTH, LONGITUDE 17°34′ WEST

We often danced in the bar at night. We had already seen all the videos and even the ecstasies of *Trouble Down Below* palled after the third showing. So after a few drinks the men brought tapes from their cabins, we listened to the music for a while, and then someone would shout 'Come *on*,' and we would heave ourselves from the low swivel chairs and begin to bop.

Keith had reported fit for duty at Afternoon watch, but his recovery from malaria was only mildly celebrated by the men that night. Jimmy was on the wagon and being vindictive. Doug received no free drinks tonight – on the wagon Jimmy's application for voluntary redundancy was never raised.

'Are the results for Billy's Master Mariner's through yet?' Jimmy asked, contriving at a casual enquiry. 'Well, if he hasn't got his certificate that's him out, anyway. Any excuse and they'll make a mate redundant. Got a cig, Doug?'

Roger was busy describing to the First Mate the ivory carving he had bought in Douala.

'It's a small replica of Gandhi.' He cupped his hands to demonstrate the size.

'It's that like him you can see it the minute you look at it. Everyone knows it. I wanted to buy two – one of him sitting crosslegged and one of him standing with a stick. But I could only afford one. I bought the one with a stick of course,' he said, asking to be congratulated for his wise choice.

Someone shouted 'Music!', and Keith put on a tape. Doug started the dancing, bouncing energetically around the saloon and tugging at Jimmy's shirtsleeves, trying to get him to abandon his position leaning against the bar. But Jimmy never danced, not even when he was off the wagon.

Soon Steve joined in, and Ramiro and Jesus were partnering each other in a half-disco, half-Mexican folk dance which involved a great deal of looping of arms and clapping. A space was cleared for them, and Ramiro skipped around the saloon while Jesus stood waiting where Ramiro had last dropped him until his arm was linked up and he was sent spinning again.

Keith shouted out, 'Liven up a bit, Jesus!', then leapt from behind the bar, pushing Ramiro out of the way and whirling Jesus violently round and round until he looked quite sick.

When the tape ran out the cry went up 'More! More!' and I darted to the stereo and pushed in my *Best of Soul Beat* tape.

> I can't wait one more day
> Tomorrow is too far away
> To feed my deep desire

The men began to wiggle their limbs as if warming up for an aerobics class.

> Honey – Get your loving
> Honey – Get your loving
> Honey – Get your loving
> Now! Now! Now! Now!

The seamen's pelvises thrust forward beneath their tropical uniforms. The half a dozen middle-aged men looked as if they were about to give birth en masse.

> Get your loving!
> Get your loving!
> N-n-n-n-ow!
> N-n-n-

The music stopped abruptly. Roger, hunched over the stereo, had ejected the *Best of Soul Beat* and was putting on Michael Jackson.

'That's better,' he said with the air of having competently executed a difficult task. 'Let's have something decent to dance to.'

The pelvises wound up again.

'Beat it! Beat it! Beat it! Beat it! Beat it! Beat it! Beat it! Beat it! Beat it! Beat it!' bellowed the seamen, thrusting in time to the chorus.

In another place, the scene before me would have made me laugh. But here I imagined the officers were performing a ritual dance in preparation for battle, and it was me on whom they had declared war. I tried to tell myself that it was only a disco dance and just Michael Jackson, but as I tried to drink from my can the beer missed my mouth and slopped down the front of my boilersuit. Had Roger chosen this song deliberately? The words bounced around my brain – *disappear, leave, go, beat it!*

I put the can down carefully on the table and pretended to be having a great time, joining in the party by swinging about in my swivel chair. Only Jimmy and I were not lost in the dance. Jimmy's eyes were glazed as he leant against the bar, looking blankly out at a saloon full of bopping seamen as if at an empty room. Doug had given up tugging at his shirtsleeves and was gyrating wildly, covering a great deal of ground.

Michael Jackson's voice continued to scream out threats and warnings. The words seemed to be aimed directly from the speakers at me, and awakened all my fears. I thought I had been accepted on board, but perhaps the men were only being polite and really wanted rid of me. I was nothing but an unwelcome intrusion into their private masculine world.

'Beat it! Beat it! Beat it!' shouted the seamen.

I had believed I could brush off the officers' occasional comments. But the combined forces of the Chief Engineer and the King of Pop were too much for me. I steadied my swivel chair and knocked back the rest of my beer. There was nowhere to go except back to my cabin.

As if compensating for the rigid order of the ship, my cabin had descended into chaos. The smell from the bridle was getting stronger, and the hot-water tap in my shower hadn't been working for several days. I had mentioned the fact to Jimmy, who said he would arrange to get it fixed. I was told, now there was no ship's carpenter, that it was the Chief Engineer's responsibility to make sure all the bathrooms were in working order.

The next afternoon there was a knock at my cabin door. It was the affable First Mate, John, who announced cheerily, 'Come to fix your tap!'

With his head bent over the shower attachment, his voice echoed around the bathtub. 'Of course, Roger should be doing this, but he's in a bit of a mood with you for changing his tape.'

'*I* didn't change *his* tape.'

'Oh, well.' The First never took sides, and it was hopeless to enrol him as a partisan. He just agreed with whoever he was talking to.

Later I bumped into Steve.

'Heard you and Roger have had a bit of a tiff,' he said, obviously pleased. Here was more evidence, as far as Steve was concerned, that I might shake things up a bit.

'What about?' I said, in a hopeless attempt to appear uninterested.

'About the tape.'

'What about the tape?' I wasn't about to let Steve goad me into criticising the Chief Engineer.

I had read in an old *Seafarer* that 'small tensions tend to develop in the confined space of a working vessel,' which was comforting. A ship's doctor had also once explained to me how the tiniest medical problem can lose all proportion in the confined quarters of a vessel. On board a boat, with no one to reassure you otherwise, you can easily become convinced that the smallest blemish is the first sign of some fatal skin disease which you will have to suffer all alone in your cabin. I myself had started to draw diagrams of my legs, marking on them where I had moles, and planned to chart any changes I noticed on a daily basis. By the side of my sketches of each limb I had jotted down notes – 'Few freckles on back of calf', 'Front shin, dark brown mole', 'Wart in middle of second toe.'

I also began to develop strange psychosomatic symptoms. The following day, my hands and feet went slowly numb. I plunged them under the hot shower, but nothing happened. Convincing myself that this was the first sign of total paralysis, I went down to the bar, feeling as if I were walking along the alleyway in very thick woolly socks. It was Forenoon watch, so Jimmy was in the galley preparing lunch and Billy was on the bridge. Only Keith and Tim, the Second Engineer, were drinking. I had nodded at Tim in the saloon and learnt that he lived in a house called Harbour Villa, and that he regarded me as an intrusion on board. A purser once warned me, 'When a stranger joins a ship, seamen are inclined to think they have a spy in the camp.' I was 'in' with the Old Man, Tim obviously thought, and, like a teacher's pet, to be despised and mistrusted.

Tim had a dark droopy moustache which made him look as if he should be wearing a cowboy hat and might pull out a pistol at any moment. I felt as if I was in a scene from *On the Lone Plain*.

'I can't feel my feet,' I said miserably, propping myself up in the doorway. I regretted opening my mouth the moment I had spoken.

The two men looked at me with mock concern and tightened their lips, trying very hard not to laugh. They obviously thought me quite mad, although not dangerous.

'I can't feel my hands either,' I moaned on, unable to stop making even more of a fool of myself.

The men turned back to their beers, stifling their sniggers, and I shuffled off, sniffling loudly. I lay spreadeagled on my bed with my feet and hands propped up on pillows, breathing deeply. Within an hour, I could wiggle my fingers and toes.

Some go to sea to find themselves. There is something entirely different about a sea voyage to any other sort of journey. No one ever took a train, or drove a car, or made an aeroplane flight to discover who they really were and what they truly wanted. But I had not joined the *Minos* on any quest for self-knowledge. I had just wanted to travel home slowly and comfortably amongst my own kind.

But the longer I stayed on board, the further away I was travelling from all that was familiar to me in Britain. All normal reference points had disappeared – the hour, the day, the distance between work and home, the division between men and women. There were no relations, friends or lovers nearby to link me into a network of relationships and make me someone's daughter, neighbour and girlfriend. On the ship I was a steersman, and there was nowhere to escape to, nowhere to go home to except the ship herself. The old order of my life was meaningless, and a new one had taken its place –the order of the ship. I wasn't finding myself, but losing myself at sea, becoming someone I had never been on land. I felt more distant from who I was in Britain than I had ever felt in Africa.

I was writing up these thoughts in my log, interwoven with

memos to myself not to get so agitated by what I now regarded as Roger's attempts to make me unpopular amongst the men, when there was a firm knock. The Captain, wearing a gold-braided peaked cap and white gloves, flanked by Jimmy and Roger, also wearing caps but without the braid, stood at the door. They faintly resembled an execution squad. Michael Jackson's advice swam around my head. We must be hundreds of miles from land. What could they do to me?

'Sure to be nice and tidy here!' announced the Captain, leading his men into my cabin as if into battle.

Roger made straight for the bathroom. Was my cabin going to be ransacked? Was this a stowaway search? Did they think I was concealing drugs?

Jimmy looked ridiculous in his cap, which was too small and sat at a tilt on top of his large head. As he looked up at the ceiling, the spare flesh on his face turned to the texture and colour of concrete.

'Take. My. Towel. Out. Of. The. Air. Conditioning. Vent. PLEASE,' he spat.

I scrambled up on to the bed and pulled out the towel, revealing watery green stains where the damp air had filtered through. The bed was unmade, and heaps of dirty clothes occupied the only chair and bedside table. Since leaving Monrovia I had intended to do a wash and had sorted into 'coloureds' and 'whites' but never made it to the laundry room.

The three officers marched around my cabin like clockwork soldiers. Jimmy opened my cupboard doors. A dusky whiff of Africa rose out from my luggage. Roger ran his finger along my desk and over the open log. Could he read my account of last night? Could he read what I had written about him?

They regrouped at the door with their hands clasped behind their backs, the Captain standing stiffly in front of his Chief Engineer and Catering Officer.

'Need a bit of order in here,' he snapped, and marched his troops off.

'We used to do it every day,' said Jimmy. 'But now we've too much work on. The Chief has to be downstairs. There's only me and George in the galley. But the Old Man and me used to go around all the cabins checking. It was the daily inspection.'

A seaman is supposed to keep his cabin shipshape. His bed must be made, his bathroom scrubbed and his desk dusted every day. I had mistakenly thought that my cabin was my private place on board where I could do, and be, whatever I wanted.

'And what was that stench in the cupboard?' asked Jimmy.

'Africa,' I said.

Chapter Twelve

LATITUDE 22°38' NORTH, LONGITUDE 17°34' WEST
TO LATITUDE 27°08' NORTH, LONGITUDE 15°36' WEST

For the rest of the day I kept to my cabin. I spent the afternoon cleaning the bathroom. Then I slunk around to the laundry room. The wooden drying racks were covered with Y-fronts.

When my phone rang I ignored it. Although it looked like an ordinary phone and had a normal dialling tone, it only made calls within the ship. By the evening I was wallowing in my misfortune. I wanted to talk to someone who lived in a house, went to work on a bus, and knew the time and which day of the week it was.

I pulled my tin trunk from the back of the cupboard and took out my Kaduna cotton wrapper skirt and headtie. The Yoruba women wound the wrapper anti-clockwise about their waists and secured it with a tuck on the left hip. The headtie was worn in a turban with the two loose ends fluted out like the wings of a bird.

I sat dressed like this for hours under the airconditioning vent, now bellowing cold air into my cabin, remembering the humidity of the West African coast. Africa had seemed full of dangers and very foreign when I had been travelling about it, but from the ocean it seemed a safe, enchanting place. A few moments after leaving the veranda which had served as my room and home in Nigeria, my skin would be damp with sweat and a fine red dust would cling to my ankles and arms, like the henna the Hausa women from the North painted on the soles of their feet. When I reached Dugbe market, I would buy a mineral from one of the hawkers, and perhaps a boiled egg. If there was salt fish, I would buy some, because you never knew when you would be able to get it again. I would find who had the rice with the least stones – pebbles are added to increase the weight – and then employ a small boy to sift through the grains. There were always some small stones left, and it was easy to break a tooth on them. By the time I had walked home, the houseboy, Kayode, would be back from school and I would send him to fetch some water so I could wash off the red dust.

When I calculated everyone was either on duty or drinking in the bar, I ventured on deck. It was a black night with a nursery rhyme moon. I could hear music coming up from the saloon: it sounded like my *Best of Soul Beat* tape. I turned around to see Doug staring at me wide-eyed. Our gazes locked for a second, before he spun about and scurried inside as if he'd seen a ghost.

I retreated to my cabin and unwound my headtie and wrapper, folding them neatly back into the tin trunk. Africa had no place on this ship; perhaps I should just be a woman, as I was in Britain. I took out my Little English Number dress which I hadn't worn since waving goodbye to Sarah on Apapa quay. 'You'll be all right if you just keep away from them,' she had warned. With my increased weight from the seaman's diet, the waistband was tight.

I felt as if I was in fancy dress. A woman doesn't belong on a cargo vessel. The sea is said to grow angry at the sight of her, although gales subside if a naked woman appears, which is why a ship's figurehead often shows a woman with her breasts bared.

In a *Seafarer* magazine I read a prizewinning essay by a retired master about two women whom he had served with at sea. 'Jane' and 'Rachel' – ('Jane and Rachel are pseudonyms' confided the captain, as if revelation of a seafaring past would damage their reputations) – sounded as if they were being introduced as contestants in a local beauty contest:

Jane is a very feminine 28-year-old navigating officer with ten years' experience in tankers, bulkers and cargo ships. She is petite, blue-eyed and blonde and has a wonderful sense of humour. This most attractive lady is presently at college studying for her Master's ticket and is engaged to a fellow navigator.

Rachel, who is 26, is an attractive ex-radio officer with several years' experience in cargo ships and container ships. She married a fellow officer and has left the sea but, with a sympathetic and friendly nature, she is ideally suited to her new job of teaching would-be radio officers at college.

Rachel's experience at sea had not been happy:

Whenever there was a full moon someone would call her on the phone in the middle of the night and make heavy breathing noises. Personal belongings would go missing from her cabin and sometimes someone was there when she awoke. Eventually, she set a trap for her tormentor and discovered his identity – the Captain!

The essayist assured the reader that this type of incident was extremely rare. It was 'shoreworkers' and 'randy Arabs in the Persian Gulf' that were the real nuisance, not men on board. He also warned:

A male environment might have been expected to sexually stimulate a lone girl but this was not the case. One of them said that, if anything, the opposite happened, while the other used to crush any feelings of that nature as it would be a very dangerous game to play aboard a ship.

The one female at home on the water was the ship herself. It is only the British who think their ships are feminine – French boats are male – and this strange fact exercises the minds of maritime historians, who regard it as a problem worthy of academic papers and submissions to 'Notes and Queries' in *The Mariner's Mirror*. It is particularly awkward, they feel, when the ship has a masculine name. 'Old James, she use to yaw to starboard . . . ' sounds odd to their academic ears, and they search for a reason why the English language has been genderised in this particular instance. They note that in times of war enemy boats are referred to as 'he', and wonder why this is. It is occasionally suggested in a learned journal that this matter should be tackled head on and references to ships be standardised. The solution is simple: all ships should be referred to as 'he'.

I went on deck for a breath of fresh air. The sea was now heaving gently. The nights were growing cool, and I shivered in my sundress. In the quiet I heard footsteps and turned round to see Doug climbing the companionway. He started as he saw me leaning

against the deckrail. One minute I had appeared before him dressed
as a heavy madam market trader, the next as if I were on my way to
a tea party in the Home Counties. He scrambled back down the
companionway.

Back in my cabin I pulled off my dress and pulled on my
boilersuit. While I had been hiding Billy might have changed the
clocks. There could even have been another pub lunch if Jimmy had
felt like hurrying along the week. I couldn't be sure what time or
day of the week it was. I might be out of sync with everyone else on
board.

As I strode towards the door there was another firm knock. The
Captain stood with a pile of newspapers balanced on his out-
stretched arms like a waiter delivering room service.

'Working?' he said, nodding towards the airconditioning vent.

'Yes, sir.'

'Try stuffing these in it. Keep out the wind.'

'Thank you, sir.'

The sun rose slowly over the sea, bleeding into the water. It was
Morning watch, and the ship was quiet. The Second Engineer went
on duty below decks and Quist was on the bridge wing keeping
lookout. The First Mate and a sailor were holding the bridge. As the
sun crept up, the ship began to stir and the boatswain came from
below to receive his instructions for the day. The Mate switched off
the lamp over the chart table and consulted the *Nautical Almanac*.
Tonight there would be a total eclipse of the moon.

Edmund Halley, who gave his name to the most famous of
comets, was an early advocate for observing lunar occultations as
the most reliable method of calculating longitude at sea. In 1719, he
set up a research programme to discover the longitude of the Cape of
Good Hope. Halley recorded the local time of an eclipse at the Cape
and the time of the same eclipse at the meridian. By this method, he
noted that the toe of Africa lay eighteen and a half degrees east of
Greenwich.

Halley was a relentless and fanatical worker. Recognising that
the existing lunar tables contained inaccuracies, he set about
looking for consistency in the errors. In 1731, aged seventy-five, he
announced to the Royal Society that he had taken 'with my own
eye without any assistance or interruption . . . 1500 observations of

the Moon'. Although meticulous, Halley did not conduct his enquiries with cold scientific dedication, but in a state of rapture. He seemed exactly like the sort of man I was sailing with, possessing enormous technical skills and thorough to the point of pedantry, yet in awe of the very thing which he was trying to codify and control – the skies and the ocean. During his long lifetime, Halley had been both master of the *Paramour* and Astronomer Royal, a seaman and a stargazer.

Roger approached me while I was taking my swim that afternoon. I shivered at the prospect of him peeling off his boilersuit and slithering in over the side like a giant beaver. He paced around and around the postage-stamp pool, and eventually coughed out his peace offering, 'Would you like to see the engine room?'

He was standing well back as if worried I might splash him. 'I'll show you around if you like.'

With each deck we descended, the thud of the pistons grew louder and the temperature rose. Several decks down, we arrived in the engine room, which was not a room at all but a warren of chambers with enormously high deckheads, and metal bulkheads and doors.

The *Minos* was assuming the proportions of a continent rather than a single country, the landscape was so varied. Above decks, the bulkheads were flimsy vinyl partitions and linoleum ran along the alleyways. The only sound was the rumble of the engines from below and the swish of the sea. The airconditioning kept the temperature at that of a fine English spring morning.

Below decks was hot, steamy and deafeningly noisy. Enormous metal machines pounded and hissed like caged monsters.

Roger was a droll guide.

'This is a piston,' he shouted close to my ear. 'And here are two Africans painting.'

The chipping gang were working on the waist-thick pipes which ran along the ceilings and walls of the connected chambers. When they chipped to one end of a pipe, they began painting at the other. Within a few months, that paint would have to be chipped off again.

Steve was bending over one of the shuddering machines, wielding an oversized spanner which he held up and waved towards me. It was far too noisy to talk. Under the tall deckheads and amongst the thundering machinery, the Fourth Engineer looked very young and very fragile.

'Steve fixing the generator,' said Roger.

The engineers below decks even looked different from the mates above. Their boilersuits were smeared with oil. I never saw a mate anything but spotless. Above decks the fear was foundering or hitting another vessel, and prevention of collision occupied most of the mates' energy. Below decks, the greatest fear was fire. Each chamber was hermetically sealed with a thick metal door secured with a wheel. The only colour amongst the machinery was the fire extinguishers. In the control room, a panel of alarms gave the location of any fires. Other panels were covered with similar rectangular boxes which lit up green or red. On each box was a message – WTR LVL HGH, AR CNDTNG OVR FLW, TRPPD – as if the signwriter suffered from a speech impediment which prevented him from pronouncing vowels.

A record of our passage was being kept below decks which bore no resemblance to the Deck Log on the bridge. Entries in the control room's Movement Book read:

> Slow Astern. 0234 hours.
> Stop. 0243 hours.
> Half Astern. 1418 hours.

'The Movement Book,' said Roger flatly. 'Records everything important that happens on the ship.'

I felt cold on deck after the heat of the engine room. We were waiting for the eclipse. As slowly as the sun had risen in the morning, it cast the earth's shadow over the moon. The officers were hanging over the deck rail. Doug offered me a cigarette and we chatted about the day as more and more of the moon disappeared.

'I was down with Roger in the engine room,' I said. 'Bloody hot down there.'

'I don't know how they stand it,' said Doug. 'Makes you think. Must be some metal in those engineers to put up with all that commotion.'

'Mmm.'

'What do you think about Jimmy?' he asked.

'What about Jimmy?'

'About the reply.'

'You mean his redundancy?'

'Haven't you heard?' said Doug. 'A message came through this afternoon. He's out.'

A thin crescent of yellow arched in the sky. Then there was no longer a moon.

Chapter Thirteen

Billy said he would show me how to navigate from the stars. The night was crisp and clear, perfect conditions for discovering the sky.

From the wing of a ship's bridge, with the closest artificial light hundreds of miles away, the night sky takes on an entirely different character to that in a city. From London, I had looked up as if at a flat board above me, with the stars pinned on it in simple patterns. I would search for a familiar constellation: the Plough, the Great Bear, the Seven Sisters.

At sea, the night sky arched above us in a huge dome, as if we were sitting under the roof of an almighty cathedral. As we recorded our path, the dome rotated above us. All bearings of celestial objects are taken with the presumption that the observer is at the centre of the universe, which seemed entirely appropriate from where I was standing.

Billy pointed out the stars to me. Sirius, the brightest in the sky, only nine light years away and white hot. The brightness of a star is measured in six magnitudes, one being the greatest and clearly visible to the naked eye, six being the least visible. Sirius is so bright that it has a minus magnitude of −1.6. Next Billy pointed to Vega, with twice the surface temperature of the sun, and Pollux in Gemini of the first magnitude. My vision of the stars developed from a sprinkling of pretty white dots to recognising individually shaped stellae with varying brightnesses and discernible characteristics. An exceptional observer can assess the magnitude of a star simply by looking at it. Stars are also coloured; that night on the bridge, Vega gleamed with a distinctive bluish tint.

Inserted into the *Nautical Almanac* is an 'Index to Selected Stars'. It does not list them under constellations like an inventory of local pubs, but under their individual names, wonderful and mysterious, like Miaplacidus, Markab, Al Na'ir and Zubenelgenubi. The *Almanac* gives their magnitude and their declination, that is their angle north or south of the celestial equator. Al Na'ir, for example, is South forty-seven degrees.

As Billy pointed to the stars and gave them names, he talked in a voice which startled and disturbed me. He sounded totally normal. He wasn't an officer commanding a cadet, or a burly seaman mocking a young woman's ignorance of the sea, or a man feeling awkward because he was alone in the company of a female. He was talking to me as if to a friend, or as if we were shipmates. I hadn't been spoken to like that for weeks. I had forgotten how natural conversation could be.

'There!' he pointed to a streak of light spinning across the mighty dome. 'There! A shooting star!'

'Satellite,' said the Mate at breakfast the next day. 'It was a satellite.'

'Shooting star,' I said. If I repeated it forcefully enough, it must be true.

'Satellite,' said the Mate gently. In his terms, this counted as a full-blown argument. 'It disappeared, so it's a satellite.'

He picked up his plate and left the table. The Mate had won.

'Lovely morning,' said the Captain.

I now realised that the Captain's 'Lovely morning' was more than a mere pleasantry. He was informing us that it was forecast to remain calm, and we should have a fine day's sailing ahead of us. When you are on a ship, the weather is no longer a polite topic of conversation, it is integral to the pattern of your day. If the sea brewed up, the Captain would come up on to the bridge and a careful watch would be kept down in the engine room. But this morning it was truly lovely, mild and breezy. 'Moderate sea, low northwesterly swell, cloudy and clear, vessel pitching easily,' recorded the Deck Log.

'Australia is a lovely place,' the Captain continued. He often began his conversation with this phrase. It gave no indication whatsoever of the line of argument that would follow. He could be about to give an opinion on just about anything.

'Bad to their blacks, though. What do you call them?' He barked out the question as if giving Doug and me an oral examination in human geography.

Doug nodded his head sagely, agreeing with any pearls of wisdom that might drop from his superior officer's lips. No one ever argued with the Old Man.

'Aborigines!' the Captain cried, triumphant. There followed a list of other people who inhabited the great Down Under. Koreans, Vietnamese, Chinese and Greeks, the last delivered with an arch of his grey eyebrows which indicated that these were surely the worst of a bad lot. The Australian Department of Immigration had made a horrible blunder in allowing them in.

'The Italians and the Yugoslavs want to make Australia into a republic. Can't blame them. They've got no allegiance to the Crown,' he continued.

The Queen, still a young woman in the photograph hanging above the tables in the officers' mess, shone down on us in her tiara.

The Old Man, undaunted, continued his one-sided conversation. 'But you know what people say if they turn it into a republic. Be like Argentina.'

News about Argentina had seeped through into my cabin that morning from the BBC World Service on the Captain's radio. I had heard snippets of alleged tortures, disappearances and bloody demonstrations.

'White man in the southern hemisphere.' This was a philosophical statement on the part of the Captain, recognisable as such by the absence of a verb. It was delivered with an air of great finality, as if some deep and troubling issue which had been plaguing philosophical minds for centuries had eventually been solved around the dining table in the officers' mess of MV *Minos*.

I recorded it in my log, as I did all the commanding officer's pronouncements, for further contemplation. I was trying to construct a system of beliefs from his brief verbless utterings, much like Ludwig Wittgenstein's celebrated *Philosophical Investigations*. I took the words 'White man in the southern hemisphere', together with their solemn mode of delivery, to infer that northern

Europeans were doomed to fail in their attempts to settle below the equator. The examples of Australia and Argentina made this clear. It was the Captain's own succinct expression of the whole *Heart of Darkness* thesis.

The next notes in my log of the Captain's theory on the condition of the white man read:

> *South Africa. White man should give over power slowly. Otherwise he'll lose altogether. Like Zimbabwe. Pulled out twenty years too early.*

This seemed to directly contradict his earlier statement. I battled over the two propositions in the privacy of my cabin, looking for further clues in earlier utterances. It never occurred to me, as it never occurred to any of the officers, to lean towards the Old Man as he supped his porridge from a soup spoon and ask, 'Excuse me, sir, but what exactly do you *mean*?'

I was absorbing more and more technical data, and gaining confidence in the ship's language. I no longer felt apprehensive before going up to the bridge. I looked forward to it. The seamen had stopped running out on deck when I took over the wheel to inspect the wake. Steering a 21,000-ton cargo vessel was just something I did each day.

Only occasionally did I remember, as I stood at the tiny wheel and looked out across the ocean, what an enormous distance I had travelled. The *Minos* often felt as if she were stationary. The only sense of movement was from side to side as we rolled, as if we were on a funfair ride, tossing about on the same pivot and never going anywhere. Yet I was far away from the person who had boarded at Apapa. It wasn't only my newfound technical competence; I was physically different too. Jella was considerably fatter.

When I had boarded the *Minos*, I had been glad I was not buxom. It could only have led to trouble if I had been the sort of woman the officers could have imagined they might fancy. But the Kru considered me horribly underweight and were determined to do something about it.

West African men like their women large and fleshy. In Nigeria, I was often asked with genuine concern if I was ill – Did I perhaps have a touch of fever? – and a pile of pounded yam would be placed in front of me. Starch is the basis of the Nigerian diet, and it arrives in a variety of disguises, many unpalatable to Europeans. The root cassava is made edible by grating into 'gari', before it is cooked and mashed into 'eba', which looks and tastes like congealed wallpaper paste. As if the texture were not difficult enough, these starches also come in a variety of colours not normally associated with things that are considered delicious: yam flour starch, known as amala, is a dirty black. The most digestible of all, if you can get it, is rice.

West African women like to have regal figures of which they can be proud. They wind vivid wrappers around their waists which they continually play with, tucking them in, smoothing them down, hitching them up, so it is impossible not to notice their splendid hips. Amongst the Ibibio in southeastern Nigeria a weighty woman is so admired that they fatten up girls in secluded 'fattening houses' to make them attractive to prospective husbands. In the fattening house, the young Ibibio woman is pampered and waited upon, fed colossal meals of eba and pounded yam, and smeared with clay and oil to prevent her losing any weight through perspiration. The young woman may not leave the compound until, dark and oiled, she emerges several months later to be displayed in her full, fat beauty.

In the seclusion of the *Minos*, I grew round and lovely. Seamen used to receive different rations according to their rank: the higher an officer was in the ship's hierarchy, the larger meals he would be served by the stewards. On the *Minos* the principle was reversed. As the most junior member of crew, I was fed the most. When Abu or Mohammed took my order from the white menu card at dinner, they would let George in the galley know it was for me.

'One more for Jella!' George would reply, and give me an extra-large helping. The seamen's helpings were gargantuan, and extra-large on the ship was the diet of a giant on land. So while the First Mate was picking his way through his Trout au Buerre, I would have two fish on my plate, one always threatening to slither through the sea of buttery sauce on to the white tablecloth. If I tried to miss out a course – 'No thanks, I'll skip meat tonight and go straight on to dessert' – it would appear in front of me nevertheless, and I would be shamed into eating it in front of the officers. By the time I arrived back in Britain, I would be the ideal figure for a

Nigerian woman and far too fat for European fashion. I had a splendid belly, round, high and hard, just like the ladies in the Ibibio fattening houses. And just like the officers of MV *Minos*.

I found Jimmy in the galley unpacking boxes of wine. He was preparing for the next event in our social calendar, the barbecue.

'What sort is it?' I asked, nodding towards the wine boxes.

'Very good sort. That's what sort it is.' Jimmy was stone cold sober.

'Vin du Pays. A region of France, you know,' he said with such a flourish that it only emphasised how unsure he was of his answer. He turned to more certain subjects.

'Potage Americano. Chino Chillo. Eskimo Nell. Trout au Buerre. What do you think of that, then?' He brandished the dinner card before me. 'Pretty good, eh?'

'Delicious,' I said. 'Eskimo Nell's one of my favourites.'

'Not bad, is it? Made it up myself. A ball of sausage meat, wrap some bacon round it, and drop the whole lot in batter. The gravy's good too.'

'Why don't you try it without the batter?' I offered, as if at a Women's Institute coffee morning. I was making idle chat, but to Jimmy I had questioned the one thing of which he was proud, his innovative menu.

Why don't you try it without the batter?

I had never seen Jimmy anything but upright, leaning against the steel surfaces in the galley, resting on his desk in the purser's office, or propping up the bar. Now he sat down. His body collapsed like a concertina, and his fine height and burliness shrivelled away. He looked like a tiny old man.

I admired Jimmy; he was a good man, and a fine representative of his profession. I'd believed him when he said, over and over in the officers' saloon, that old Jimmy Patterson didn't mind being made redundant, there was plenty else that he could do.

'Aaaaaaah,' he let out an enormous sigh as if releasing air through a valve. His body was so crumpled that there was hardly anything left of him in the chair.

I looked at him with undisguised horror, as if I had come across the Chief Steward in the nude, without the protection of his Merchant Navy tropical uniform, and discovered that he was just a fifty-three-year-old man with pleated, sagging flesh. My legendary seaman had disappeared. I grabbed my coffee mug and ran.

The next time Jimmy and I met was in the bar. The Chief Steward was off the wagon, reinflated, and waxing lyrical about Marks & Spencer seconds. He'd set up a business in them. There was a great demand in Liverpool for M & S ladies' hosiery with ladders, knickers with no elastic, Y-fronts with the Y at the back, he joked. The variations Jimmy conjured up in M & S second-lines were wonderful and obscene.

Doug joined in. 'Nighties with nipple holes!' he shouted, and we all jeered. The bar was still a good place to be when Jimmy was off the wagon.

We were sailing through the Canary Islands, making our way through the forty-five-mile-wide channel between Gran Canaria and Fuerteventura. It was the first time we had seen land for several days. It is many years since ships *en route* to West Africa had called at Las Palmas for bunkering, and the Canary Islands' links with Africa have long been broken. The summit of the volcano which forms Gran Canaria was smothered by cloud, as if it were still smoking. It was dusk, and the lower slopes sparkled with yellow lights. The island looked strangely like a liner at sea with her deck lights on, steaming past us on the port quarter.

By the following morning, land was well out of sight, but there was plenty to look at. A great deal happens while you are at sea, although it takes some time to appreciate this. At first the ocean looks vast and empty. Other vessels occasionally come into view, but they are just grey silhouettes in the distance and not particularly interesting. But after a while I noticed changes in the sea, and I could interpret the shadows of the passing ships. First I saw how the water changed colour frequently, even from hour to hour. I began to read the sea like a landscape and find in it as many features as I would have on a drive through the countryside. When Doug leant against the console during one Dogs and said, 'I like the water. It's not like other views. There's always something to look at,' I heartily agreed with him.

As we sailed north, we spotted more and more ships. These were often the topic of conversation at mealtimes. The men would relate details of vessels they had seen that day, and this would stir up memories of earlier sightings. What had to me appeared as a simple outline on the horizon, to the seamen told a story that could be traced around the world.

'Car carrier,' the Captain announced at breakfast, nodding towards the porthole. 'Usually comes from Japan, but something that size could easily get through Suez.'

He paused, his spoonful of porridge suspended mid-air, and turned over the Admiralty charts in his head, stored as neatly as those in the narrow drawers below the chart table on the bridge. 4101 Lisbon to Freetown, 4209 Freetown to Luanda, 4203 Luanda to . . . until he reached the port of Kobe. He wondered why this vessel through the porthole had not followed the shortest course to her destination, using the Suez canal, instead of adding five thousand miles to her journey by rounding the Cape of Good Hope.

'Must be congested. Suez.' He was satisfied with his explanation. From a silhouette on the horizon, the Captain had deduced happenings three thousand miles away.

Forenoons I was chatting to Billy on the bridge.

'Have you seen Jimmy?' I asked.

'In the galley?'

'Nope.'

'In the bar?'

'Uh-huh.'

'God knows, then. He could be anywhere.'

It was as easy to disappear within the confines of the ship as in the streets of a major town.

We didn't know, but Jimmy was busy planning his retreat to Africa.

Chapter Fourteen

I found the Chief Steward the next morning, resting against the stainless steel surfaces in the galley, chatting to George. He greeted me with a comfortable smile.

'There's something about the place,' he said, 'which makes you keep coming back. The number of times I've heard a man say "I've had enough, I'm going home. Never again, never again am I coming back to that goddam coast". Then six months later there he is, signed up for another West African voyage. There's something about the place, I don't know.'

Jimmy had often bragged about his dislike of Africa. He particularly enjoyed telling me this in front of George, whom he also claimed to thoroughly detest. 'Even George, even *George* nicks the tea bags,' he'd once told me, disgusted at his Chief Cook for stooping so low.

Leaning against the counter, Jimmy seemed happy and relaxed. So I asked him a question that had been on my mind for some time.

'What are you going to do?'

He replied instantly. 'I'll go for a job in Africa.'

I was astonished. 'Africa?'

'Lagos, maybe.'

'*Lagos?*'

Niggernash, I thought. Surely Jimmy wasn't going to work for Niggernash? What had happened to M & S seconds?

'I'll see what's going there,' he continued chirpily, shifting to his other elbow. His stomach lazily redistributed itself from one side to the other, long after his elbow and head had already arrived at their new positions.

'But first I'll take a holiday.'

'Tenerife?' I asked. Jimmy had shares in a house in the Canary Islands. 'I've heard it's lovely there.'

'No, Freetown,' he said. 'I'll go for a well-earnt six weeks' rest in Freetown.'

George was chopping the chile peppers. It must be Tuesday, for there was a cauldron of fish heads bubbling on the stove. Tuesday was Fish Pepper Soup.

'I'll stay with George and his family. Did you know George here and me, we've known each other over twenty years. That's a long time.

'No true, George,' Jimmy turned to his Chief Cook. 'You dun go beggingo me to come, no?'

'Yes, sar!' cheered George.

I left the two old West Coasters chatting away to each other in pidgin, bemoaning that Freetown was not what it used to be.

Another important message had been relayed through Doug in the radio room. Second Engineer Tim's wife was pregnant.

Births are celebrated unreservedly on board ships – but the initial news of a pregnancy is greeted with caution. First the date of conception has to be confirmed.

'How long have you been away, Tim?' called out Roger in the bar. 'When did you say the brat's due?'

But it was Tim's first child, and he was ecstatic. He was also very, very drunk.

'Bugger off, Roger,' he said to his Chief. 'It's mine all right.'

Tim was rather good-looking and so, Keith assured me, was his wife. She had, he said with a wink, some Swedish in her. Her name was Karen.

The married younger officers – Tim, Keith and Steve – had passport-sized photographs of their wives pinned up above the desks in their cabins. Keith's wife was looking straight out of the photograph where the glass square in front of the lens in the photo booth must have been, and where Keith now sat. She had straight hair parted in the middle and a pretty, round face that could have belonged to hundreds of young women. It was the sort of photograph that might appear on a bus-pass or security card, solely for the purpose of identification. It gave away nothing but the plain physical facts about the Second Mate's wife: Mrs Keith Markham: hair – long and light brown; skin – pale; no distinguishing characteristics. It was as if Keith kept the photograph above his desk to remind him what she looked like.

I had a photograph of Liam, my man in Britain, which I had carried around West Africa and had thought of putting up above my desk. But it was taken on a beach, and showed him throwing back his curly head and laughing. Next to the photographs of the officers' wives, it would have looked obscenely intimate. So I had packed it away in the back of my cupboard along with Africa.

Keith and Steve also had pictures of their children pinned up above their desks. Twenty-three-year-old Steve, who had danced in the Douala disco, was a father of three. The pictures of Keith's two children were end-of-term school photographs, and they both wore grey uniforms with crimson piping. His son's fine blond hair had been combed so flat on his head that at first sight he looked completely bald.

'My family,' Keith had said, pointing proudly at the photographs above his desk. For eight months out of every twelve, Keith's family was no more than these strained pictures. Steve hadn't seen his daughter until she was almost four months old.

Tim's good news stirred up fond memories.

'Forgot the pill,' said Keith. The men nodded their heads in sympathy.

'Wouldn't change it for the world, mind you. Wouldn't change it for the world. She's a wonderful mother to the kids. Smashing. Just smashing.'

The officers clucked in agreement like a brood of hens.

Most seamen are hopelessly romantic about the wives they seldom see. Tucked between notices in the maritime press for courses in marine engineering, the services of accountants who specialise in seafarers' tax problems, and marine personnel employment agencies, there is a regularly running advertisement for Sovereign Flying Florist. ('Make someone pleased you read this advertisement today. Your choice of flowers flown direct from the grower in handsome white presentation boxes with your personal message.') Alongside the Flying Florist notice is a photograph of a middle-aged woman in a fiercely ironed white blouse reading from a card. She is displaying a fine set of teeth in delight at the personal message.

I myself had received a Flying Florist Single Red Rose from a seaman once. It arrived in a cellophane box lined with green feathery fern. The message, written in biro by the florist, read, 'I sailed towards a rainbow rising through the mist. Today I send a flower, for it made me think of you.' I imagine all Flying Florist messages are as sentimental.

The seamen adored their wives; they could often be heard praising their talents as mothers and homekeepers to their ship-mates. But they never said they found them sexy. If their ship was docked in Britain for a couple of days, the shipping line allowed a wife to come on board and join her husband while he was in port. The officer would put in a request to the captain for a special temporary cabin. Our cabins were roomy and furnished with a four-foot-wide single bed. The special cabins had two narrow twin beds in them.

'Twins are far more comfortable than sharing a single bed,' said Keith, 'when the wife comes on board.'

Everyone agreed.

When a seaman thinks of sex, he dreams of very different, dusky women.

At 30°48' North, 14°15' West, the airconditioning was switched off, and I removed the Captain's newspapers from the vent above my head. I smoothed them out as best I could and began to read. People seemed to be engaging in the most bizarre activities, and the newspapers to have no sense at all of what was important. Something about a pop star's mystery disease was on the front page. The weather was relegated to a tiny column on the inside back. There was no information at all about conditions at sea. Over two hundred miles off the Moroccan coast, the newspapers read like fiction.

They were also almost two months out of date, but because their content was so insignificant, this didn't bother me at all. Anyway, reading habits on board depended entirely upon what was avail-able. My initial disappointment at the choice offered in the ship's library was temporarily relieved when I uncovered a copy of *The African Queen*. But from then on it had been a lucky dip. Next came a doorstopper of a novel set during the Indian Mutiny which left the unpleasant impression that every Indian was a murderous rapist. Then I came across a well-thumbed copy of D. M. Thomas's *The White Hotel*.

'Precise, Troubling, Brilliant,' said the *Observer*'s critic on the front cover. 'To describe this novel as spine tingling in its indescribably poetic effect would be to trivialize its profoundly tragic theme,' said the *New York Times* on the back.

'Good stuff,' said Doug in the bar. 'It's done the rounds. You can have it now if you like.' The seamen regarded *The White Hotel* as first-rate pornography.

I sneaked back to my cabin with D. M. Thomas stuffed down the front of my boilersuit, worried that I might get caught by the Captain in possession of such scurrilous material. I locked my door and searched for the dirty bits, which Doug had already guided me to in the bar.

> She could feel her lover's hand touching her beneath the table cloth. Her head was spinning from their having drunk too much . . .

I lay back on my bed and thought of the Fourth Engineer.

> Her young lover's penis had been inside her even while they were struggling up the stairs . . .

Doug was right, this was very sexy stuff. It was also the only sort of passion I could safely indulge in on board the ship. Between watches, I often retreated to *The White Hotel*, in which I imagined Steve and I were having a wonderfully uncomplicated affair.

'Where's *The White Hotel*?' asked Tim in the bar.

'Jella's got it,' said Doug.

'Oh-ho-ho-ho!' roared Keith.

There was one other treasure in the ship's library, *Sir Apolo Kagwa Discovers Britain*.

In 1902, King Edward VII invited the Prime Minister of Buganda to his coronation. Sir Apolo was accompanied by his loyal secretary Ham Mukasa, who kept a remarkable diary of their journeys through darkest industrial Britain. Their first stop in London was at the Army and Navy Stores.

When we got into the shop my eyes itched with wonder at the beautiful things. I saw a room filled with people drinking tea. The people who had come there to buy things were like those who were going off to war, some going upstairs, some downstairs, and some being carried up in little rooms like the one in the hotel.

Sir Apolo, Ham Mukasa and his notebook went to see *Ben Hur* at the Drury Lane Theatre, 'a very large house, and they had put in it shelves for all the sight-seers to sit on,' and on to the circus at the Hippodrome where, 'some elephants put a man on a couch just as if he were ill, and carried him where they were told; one of them was told to fetch medicine off the table, and it did so, and gave it him to drink.' Then on to the Crystal Palace where, 'a woman showed us a machine for sweeping up the rubbish in a house, and wanted us to buy one, and we thanked her for showing it us.'

I understood Sir Apolo perfectly. In the North Atlantic, every-thing that went on in England seemed wondrous and absurd too. The honourable Prime Minister of Buganda's and the seamen's view of the world had much in common.

At 35°35′ North, 12°25′ West, west of the Strait of Gibraltar, the Captain conducted a contraband search. The boatswain's locker, the crow's nest and between the hatches were searched by the Old Man accompanied by his Chief Engineer and Catering Officer. They were looking for drugs.

'West Africa. Rife in the drug trade,' the Captain had announced at breakfast. But the Official Log recorded, 'Nothing was found.'

On Dogs the Captain ordered me to turn the ship. Readings from both the electronic and magnetic compasses contained errors. There was a place in the Deck Log for compass errors to be recorded; on most ships, this column would have stayed blank. But on the *Minos* it was assiduously filled in at every watch.

In the case of the magnetic compass, the Captain was particu-larly fastidious. If the electricity failed, he said, or the gyro compass started spinning round and round, the old-fashioned magnetic compass would be the only reliable instrument to record our course. He instructed that readings be taken from it six times a day.

'Know where the ship is then,' he said, as if the fixes from the satellite navigation system or Decca Navigator could not tell him this.

The magnetic compass deviated from true due to the soft magnetism of the earth, which varied with our latitude, and the hard iron of the ship herself. By taking celestial or solar observations and swinging the ship, it was possible accurately to calculate the compass error.

The Captain took a bearing from a star with the azimuth mirror on the magnetic compass bowl and instructed me to turn the ship to 135 degrees from 016 degrees gyro. I followed his instructions perfectly, and swelled with pride, knowing that I was part of this throbbing, living, working organism – the ship. We were being guided by the stars above and the expertise of our Master below, through the great ocean. I could not remember feeling so happy.

Once the error was calculated, it could be corrected by adjusting the iron bar above the compass. 'Modern masters', as our Captain called them, just left the compass error for the compass adjuster in port to bring back to true. The Captain was proud that we would arrive in Liverpool with good (that is, nil) deviation, and that the cost of an adjuster would be spared.

The seamen were fiercely loyal to the shipping line. Amongst themselves, they would complain about the self-service at luncheon, moan about the bloody African sailors, and whisper about the detrimental effects of cutting costs. But amongst strangers, even other seamen, the shipping line's livery was declared the finest on the ocean, her officers the best trained, her Kru crew the most hardworking and reliable.

The ship now carried a photocopying machine in the radio room – up to twenty copies of the cargo manifest could be needed for the various officials in a port of call, and a copier was an enormous timesaver. One afternoon I had taken a volume of the *Africa Pilot* and asked Jimmy if I could photocopy a few pages. I wanted to swot up on the Bight of Biafra.

'A few pages, like,' he said, and I had nodded. He was just saying that as a matter of form, I thought. It wasn't his machine and it wasn't his paper, it was the company's, and the company was making him redundant. Why should he care.

I photocopied a few pages, then found some more interesting

sections on the waters around Tema, and began to copy them too. Fifteen minutes later, when Jimmy came back up to the radio room to check on me, sheets were still rolling out of the photocopier.

Jimmy stood looking at them piling up like bank notes.

'It's not your money you're spending,' he roared. 'That's a bleeding 'nough.'

I was ashamed and silent as I tapped the stack of photocopies into a pile and hurried off with them to my cabin. Jimmy was part of the line, and the line was part of Jimmy. They had been working together since before I was born. I felt as if I had stolen money out of the Chief Steward's wallet, and wondered how I could repay him.

Preparations for the barbecue were in full swing. Roger said he would fix up a sound system. Steve, eager to match anything Roger could offer, agreed to do the decorations. The barbecue would be held outside on the boat deck. All the officers and cadets were invited – there were only a dozen of us after all – except of course the Captain. The Old Man would be confined to his cabin for the evening, but he would have a noisy night.

Perhaps the Kru were also planning a special party, two decks below. They might roast pieces of liver on sticks over the charcoal fire, drink palm wine, and shake frenetically to Zairean music. Or perhaps they would line the alleyways on the lower bridge deck as I had once seen them do, and hold an African street party.

By the time the night of the barbecue arrived, the passage from day to night had changed. It no longer suddenly went dark as it had off the West African coast, and dusk crept back. As the light faded, Steve and Roger began work on their various preparations. Roger was setting up his sound system on deck, looping the wires along the starboard rails and around the lifeboat, under which he put the speakers. Steve had found some fairy lights, and was stringing them along the port deckrails, carefully concealing them so there was no possibility of interfering with navigation lights. Both men would meet briefly at the end of their respective wires in the Mate's cabin which, as it was the closest to the door out to the deck, was being used to provide the power.

The two men worked obsessively in a tacit race. The deck became the arena for the supreme test of manhood; these simple technical tasks would decide the contest. Who was more of a man, the Fourth Engineer or his Chief? Would the deck first tremble with fairy lights, or would Michael Jackson be heard blaring out from under the lifeboat?

Every so often one of us would wander out from the saloon on deck with a beer in our hand and shout, 'Getting there yet?' which sent the two men scurrying even faster along their side of the deck, fixing wires and checking connections.

Jimmy had set up an oildrum filled with charcoal and brought up great slabs of red meat from his walk-in fridges. With Steve and Roger still furiously battling it out to the finish, Jimmy stood lazily before the oildrum, a giant fork in his hand, flipping the scorched flesh.

Eeeeeeeeeeeeee

A horrible noise came from under the lifeboat. Roger had attempted to switch on his sound system.

Steve was delighted. He walked slowly into the Mate's cabin and plugged in his lights. The deck was transformed into a suburban back garden, with pretty little candle-shaped bulbs twinkling along the fence.

'Damn,' muttered Roger, scrabbling around under the lifeboat, which started rocking violently.

The night was calm and the ship barely moved. Steve's fairy lights cast dim colours over the lifebuoys, the coils of rope, and the capstans, making them look like giant toys in a children's playground. Boxes of Special Strength Skol had been stacked up shoulder-high beside the barbecue and the Vin du Pays was mixed into a punch in a huge plastic bowl, in which floated cubes of mango and pieces of pineapple. It was going to be a long night.

The dancing soon began and Third Mate Billy grabbed the Third Engineer, Second Mate Keith grabbed the Second Engineer, cadets Ramiro and Jesus grabbed each other, and Doug grabbed me.

When ships carried crews of fifty or more, the engineers and the deck officers led separate social lives. 'Oil and water don't mix' is a favourite nautical saying. But with the cutbacks in manning levels, there was seldom more than a couple of engineers or mates off duty at the same time, and new friendships and alliances had been formed. Where once the Second and Third Mates would have been best of pals, now the Third Mate was chummy with the junior engineers, and the Chief Officer spent time in the Chief Engineer's cabin.

Roger didn't dance, but played with the sound system all evening so that in the middle of 'Love, love me do' all the electrics went, we suddenly stood still, and the gentle slap of the water which we had forgotten surrounded us, arose out of the darkness.

'Sor-ry,' came Roger's voice out from the Mate's cabin and the speakers spluttered back to life again.

Jimmy wasn't dancing either. He never did, and anyway you had to be a bit tiddly to partner Doug or Keith to songs that crooned on about love and passion, and Jimmy was on the wagon for the fourth time since I had joined the ship.

'Jell-a,' he called and handed me another cup of punch. It was my fifth at least.

When I had first seen the officers dance I had watched them with indifference and detachment. But I couldn't stand apart and coldly observe the seamen any more. Mine had not been a sudden acceptance, although there had been landmarks along the way – the smuggled mango toothpaste, the gift of a log, The Boilersuit Incident, the resumption of normal viewing on the video. I had been gradually drawn in towards the ship, and away from another far-off world. Members of a ship's crew are called her people and I had once looked on at them as an anthropologist watches a strange tribe performing an exotic rite. But the ways on board the *Minos* now seemed the proper way to go about things. And it was land, that distant country, that looked very silly indeed.

'Dea.' I felt the whispery touch of a fingertip on the back of my arm. I started at the intimacy.

I turned round towards Steve and we began to dance. I had danced with all the officers but dancing with Steve was different, and I didn't like it. This was on deck on the *Minos*, and not the fantasy of *The White Hotel*.

'They'll all be talking about us dancing tomorrow,' he said, obviously pleased. Steve often talked about the other officers as if he was not one of them, as if they were of a different tribe.

Jimmy shouted, 'Steve, Jell-a,' and waved his fork at us. Then he prodded his giant implement in the direction of the punch bowl. 'Drink?'

'Hey, look over there!' Doug was holding on to the deckrail and swaying wildly as though being tossed about by a storm. But the sea was as still as a mirror. He was pointing at a ship.

'Belgian,' he slurred. 'But from the Congo really. See those holes underneath the accommodation block? She must be carrying passengers.'

Billy asked if I'd seen Sirius, which was particularly bright that night.

It was a great party.

'Jell-a,' and I accepted another cup of punch from Jimmy. I began to feel sick. As far as I can remember, Steve helped me to the door in to the boat deck and whispered, 'Goodnight, sailor'.

I stumbled from my bed to the bathroom the next morning and searched for anything which might have an effect similar to that of a strong aspirin. If I went to see Jimmy and asked him for something from the medicine chest, within an hour my self-inflicted state of health would be all around the ship. I found the remaining Avloclor and took two. If it worked for malaria, I couldn't see why it wouldn't wipe out a mere hangover.

Some time later, lying feverishly in bed, I heard the Captain's phone ring, followed a few minutes later by the click of his door. There were certain times when the Captain would go to the bridge: at eight in the morning, to take the morning longitude, which he would tap into his pocket calculator; at noon to take latitude; and in Dogs when he exchanged information on the day's progress with the First Mate. He also often made a brief visit after dinner to check that the Third was doing his job properly. Our Captain was a man of habit, and rarely deviated from this pattern.

I focused on the clock beside my bed. 1020 hours. I laboriously calculated that at this point in the day the Old Man should be reading undisturbed in his cabin. The Third Mate, whose watch it was, must have wanted him for something special on the bridge. Perhaps we were in danger of foundering, I thought, then fell back into a rolling, nightmarish sleep.

The day was well advanced before I emerged from my cabin.

Chapter Fifteen

LATITUDE 37°48′ NORTH, LONGITUDE 11°35′ WEST
TO LATITUDE 51°30′ NORTH, LONGITUDE 0°53′ EAST

I was up for the 1230 message. Since Keith had resumed responsibility for the daily announcement over the tannoy from Billy, it was once again delivered in his usual matter-of-fact Second Mate manner:

> Our position at noon was 36°15′ North, 11°59′ West.
> We are 1025 miles from Liverpool travelling at 12 knots.
> The wear from tomorrow will be Blues.
> Repeat.
> The wear from tomorrow will be Blues.

'Blues' was long blue trousers, a white shirt with the appropriate number of bands on the epaulettes, and a black tie.

For the rest of the day I was intensely aware of the officers' knees, jutting out between the white baggy shorts and long white socks of their splendid 'Tropics' uniform, which, if the officers' caps had been replaced by pith helmets, could have been worn by earlier envoys of the British Empire. Tropics belonged to an era when West African ports were still good places to go ashore. Steve's knees were as slender as a woman's, smothered with fine blond hair and freckles. Doug's kneecaps were perfectly square like the rest of his body. Jimmy had mighty long legs, but his knees sagged a little, rippling over the top of his socks. The Old Man's were very pink.

Blues proved to be not nearly as becoming as Tropics; it was only one step up from a doorman's uniform. But the order of the 1230 message was strictly obeyed, and from that day I never saw another pair of officer's knees. If any officer had sailed into Liverpool in his Tropics and it had come to the attention of the shipping line, the Captain would have been severely reprimanded.

We had passed Cape Saint Vincent at the tip of Portugal. A huge swell caused the ship to pitch moderately. It was too cold to bronze on deck. And when the First Mate filled the pool from the ocean, it was far too icy to swim in. I dangled my legs over the side, splashing them about, hoping it would warm up and that I would have the courage to jump in. But I didn't. I had already had my last swim in the ocean.

The cold water also reminded me, as though I had been hit by an electric shock, that I had left Africa – sticky, damp, fetid Africa – far behind.

The day continued dull and shed no warmth. Then in the early evening the sun burst through and flooded the sea and the ship in an unnatural light. It was as though someone in the heavens had cried 'Cue!', and the *Minos* had run on stage with the spotlights turned full upon her. Every fibre in the coils of rope, every flake of rust peeling from the deckrails, every murmur in the water stood out in dramatic relief. The clouds rushed across the diamond blue sky in long flat cakes of pure white, before being sucked into a point just above the horizon. It was still cold on deck, and each pore on my skin stood out like a tiny crater.

Passing ships were more numerous now, and we were rarely out of sight of another vessel. We spotted plenty of Greek ships on passage through the Strait of Gibraltar and up to Scandinavian ports.

'Greeks!' the officers would tut every time they saw one, and shake their heads.

'Greeks!' – to which the expected reply was 'Greeks all right!' – made up a large part of our conversation. Since the barbecue the ship had grown very quiet. As we prepared to enter home waters, there was more work to do on the bridge and a steady watch had to be kept on the radar. There were many dangers lying ahead of us, far greater than any that had threatened so far – traffic lanes, reckless vessels, and, most of all, land.

At breakfast the Captain kept one eye on his porridge while the other strayed every few minutes towards the porthole. Even Doug seemed preoccupied; the closer we drew to home, the more messages came through to the radio room.

Most of the men also wanted to make a phone call to their wives, informing them of our ETA. Tim called Karen on the radio phone. Karen said she would change the sheets on the bed the night before he came back, just as she always did. All over Liverpool, women were giving the sitting room a quick once over with the hoover, making a final trip to the supermarket to stock up on steak and beer, and changing the sheets to welcome home their men. Doug said his wife cooked a very good steak, 'though not as good as Jimmy.'

It was five days until we were due in dock. The bar was almost empty in the evenings, with many of the officers just popping in for a quick beer then taking to their cabins.

I had my own relationship to return to. I took out the photograph of Liam and stared at it for a long time. Did I really know him? Like the passport-sized photographs pinned up above the desks in the officers' cabins, my man was no more to me than this tiny photo. I stared at him and thought, when I leave the *Minos*, this man is the person I'm supposed to know better than anyone else. I was glad I had the photo, because otherwise I could not be certain that I would recognise him. It was as if I had been allotted a complete stranger in some sort of arranged marriage, and been sent a photo of him in advance of the ceremony. He no longer seemed to be connected with my everyday life. I supposed it was the same for the officers with their wives, and there was something comforting in this.

I tried to imagine a scene where Liam and I met on the dock, hugged, and drove off in a car. He would be sitting in the driver's seat and would ask me, 'Well, what was it like, then?' But there the daydream ended, because I could never imagine how I would explain all this to him. The thought of leaving the ship and driving away with this stranger also made me horribly sad, and I would end up splashing tears all over my desk.

Perhaps in the isolation of their single-berth cabins, some of the officers were sharing these anxieties too. Not that we let each other know that anything was in the slightest bit upsetting, any more than we admitted to a fascination for dolphins or an attraction to watching the sun setting over the sea. We just all happened to have a lot of work to do in our cabins. Only the Old Man was utterly honest about his terror of the land. He announced that he had applied to have his leave cancelled and remain on board, going directly out with the *Minos* on another voyage.

Jimmy kept up a show of being cheery and seldom mentioned his redundancy. But as we neared England his attitude towards me was changing, and it annoyed me.

First he commented that I had a pimple.

'I'll get you something for that,' he said.

'It'll go away,' I answered, irritated. Why the hell was Jimmy bothered about a spot on my nose?

'I've got this stuff in the medicine chest which will do the trick. You can't go around with a pimple on your pecker.'

Then, when I was on deck with my boilersuit rolled down to my waist and just a vest underneath, he noticed the hairs under my arms.

'Jesus, what have you got there? I'll give you a razor. Never used. Disposable, like.'

'No thanks, it doesn't bother me.'

'But you can't go around with armpits like a gorilla's. It's not ladylike.'

At last one day he pleaded, 'Why don't you ever wear a *dress*?'

Jimmy had given me the boilersuit all those weeks ago. Yet it was as if he thought he had created a monster – an ugly, hermaphrodite being – and was now setting out to destroy it.

As if arising to fill the vacuum caused by the lull in our conversation, rumours began to spread about the ship. Cut off entirely from land apart from the link through Doug's radios, they must have arisen from within the *Minos* herself. Perhaps someone had heard, in the engines' endless rumbling, distinct phrases, as you hear words in the chundering of a train. One rumour rumbled up from the engine room, snaked along the alley and vibrated up the companionway until it reached the height of the Captain's cabin.

'P&O have bought ten per cent of the shipping line's shares,' said the Old Man at breakfast. 'Perhaps they'll buy up the whole fleet and make them passenger ships again. All be wearing number ones then!'

During the palmy days before the Second World War, half a million passengers had travelled with the shipping line to West

Africa every year. The *Aureol*, which made the last regular passenger service in 1972, had 296 luxury first-class cabins. Passengers could enjoy chess tournaments in the cardroom, light music in the lounge, or a cricket match on the promenade deck. On Saturday 1 October 1960, the *Calabar*'s 105 passengers celebrated Nigerian independence at an Independence Day Dinner with Pepper Soup, Beef Tournedos Africaine, Lagoon Pudding, Ibadan Gâteau and Ye Olde English Trifle. Two years later the *Calabar*, the fourth and last of her name, was sent to the breaker's yard.

A present-day cruise ship is a poor reflection of what a passenger ship used to be. Passenger ships were going somewhere and delivering goods and mail, as well as people. Cruise ships meander around the world with no real purpose. None of the officers had ever served on a cruise ship, and looked on them with some distaste. But many had served on the passenger liners.

Jimmy had started as a steward on board one of these ships. The move from passengers to cargo and containers had left the bridge and engine room relatively unchanged – the ship still had to be powered and steered. But galleys had been transformed. Once they were hives of culinary activity from which armies of waiters, cooks and assistant cooks fed dining rooms seating two hundred. The chief steward had up to three hundred men and women working under him, including the second-class lounge stewards, tourist bedroom stewards, third-class smokeroom stewards, and stewardesses to look after the lady passengers. On the *Minos*, Jimmy and George, still titled Chief Cook although there were no longer any other cooks under him, were helped at dinner by Abu and Mohammed, who waited on the officers.

The idea of taking passengers again was greeted with enthusiasm by the men, and before the end of the day the *Minos* had been mentally kitted out with a games room, gymnasium, and a grand staircase that swept up between the decks. The empty cabins had been transformed into passenger berths, and several of the more senior officers were having affairs with the wealthy widows who were occupying them. We were all grateful to the Captain for providing us with such an inspiring alternative to that which inevitably awaited us in Britain – the slow closure of the shipping line and redundancy. We were running one of the last British–West African voyages, and somewhere beneath the don't-care bravado we all knew it. And that was another reason for spending so much time in the seclusion of our cabins.

As if the Captain's comforting vision of our future found concrete form, he gave me a gift of a verdigrised brass plaque with a hole drilled in each corner. The plaque read:

CERT FOR USE OF MASTER

PASSENGERS MUST NOT HAVE ACCESS TO THIS SPACE

If there were to be passengers, they too must stay within their strictly defined limits. Everyone had a place on board.

The plaque came, the Captain said, from the ship. But the *Minos* had never carried passengers. She was a purpose-built break-bulk and containerised cargo vessel, with accommodation for forty-five officers and crew.

Another rumour had circulated amongst the ship's people.

'You going to marry Jimmy?'

George's question stunned me. I carefully put down the cup of hot water I had taken from the urn for coffee. A funny sound – a cross between a cough and someone being strangled – escaped from between my lips.

'What did you say?' I asked very gently.

'Are you going to marry Jimmy? You'd be a fine wife for Jimmy, fine, fine.'

George was beaming and nodding his head enthusiastically, as if already congratulating the lucky bride.

'Where did you get that idea from?' I was almost hoarse.

'Jimmy.'

Now we would soon be leaving the open ocean and approaching dangerous waters, the Captain announced a boat drill. At the sound of a series of short blasts on the whistle, there was to be a simulated fire in the engine room and the ship would be evacuated.

Stories of survival at sea in small boats are legendary. They are all tales of superhuman heroism, with men displaying remarkable powers of physical and mental endurance on rations that would not nourish a mouse. In such stories, the captain sits at the helm of the lifeboat, raft or dinghy. He allocates watches and divides the rations. In the best known stories, from Captain William Bligh's *A Voyage*

*to the South Seas including an Account of the Subsequent Voyage
of Part of the Crew, in the Ship's Boat* to Captain Cecil Foster's *1700
Miles in Open Boats*, the master even keeps a meticulous log, just as
if he were entering details in the Deck Log on the bridge of the vessel
he has abandoned.

In June 1923, four days after the three thousand ton SS *Trevassa*,
loaded with powdered zinc, went down in the Indian Ocean,
Captain Foster recorded the noon position of the wooden lifeboat
carrying twenty survivors:

> *Noon.* – Lat. 27 deg. 11 min. S., Long. approx. 82 deg. 39 min. E.
> True course N. 73 deg., W., 111 miles.

Then:

> *4 p.m.* – Issued milk rations. Steering about N.W. true. Wind
> hauling to Northward.

Only occasionally is there a hint that he was not partaking in a
round-the-world yacht race:

> Allchin (cook) showing signs of sickness, in spite of orders
> drank salt water, and is now complaining of great thirst, but I
> cannot satisfy him further than his ration. Day ends with rest
> of men all well and cheerful.

The moral is shining clear: the consequence of contravening a
commanding officer's orders is a slow decline into madness and
death. The reason why men have survived at sea against such
impossible odds is because the discipline and order of the ship is
transferred, without so much as a ripple, into the tiny lifeboat.

If the order 'Abandon ship!' was ever called on the *Minos*, every
man would know how to respond without hesitation. The seamen
were in a continual state of preparation for just such a calamity. So
when the alarm for boat drill was sounded, everything passed off
smoothly. The procedure for abandoning ship seemed to be regarded as a lot less taxing than setting up the barbecue, and all
hands pulled together.

I was to report to the bridge, from where the Captain would
stage-manage the drill, and I would man the battery-powered red
Emergency Phone on the console, which had a direct line to areas of
the ship strategic to safety: the steering flat, bunkering station,

alleyway adjoining the safety room, and emergency generator room.

The red phone rang. It was Roger.

'There's a fire in C section.'

'There's a fire in C section, sir,' I repeated out loud to the Captain.

'A fire in C section,' said the Captain, looking out through the glass screen towards a dot somewhere on the horizon. 'Inform the Mate.'

I called John.

'There's a fire in C section,' I said.

All through more bandying about of instructions – 'run out hoses', 'close vents', 'secure watertight doors' – the Captain stared out across the bow, his arms braced behind his back, his feet slightly apart, standing with his ship to the last.

'Man the lifeboats.'

I snapped up a lifejacket from the back of the bridge and Billy and I went down to the lifeboat deck. The officers and crew were already gathered there, and Keith was distributing lifejackets among them.

The lifeboat was suspended above the deck on a cast-iron cradle. The bottom of the cradle was mounted on rollers which, if a wire was released, ran down tracks which swung the lifeboat out from above the deck and down into the sea. The lifeboat was the same bright orange as our lifejackets. There were drain plugs in the bottom of the boats, which Keith ordered a sailor to put in, and the sailor reported back having done so.

'Your Mae West's a bit big for you,' joked Keith, referring to my inflated fluorescent lifejacket which protruded out mightily in front of me. It made it very awkward to move my arms any way but directly up and down, which made me look as if I were attempting to fly from the deck of the sinking ship, so I let them dangle helplessly at my sides like lengths of rope. I balked at the prospect of having to clamber into a lifeboat in a 42D size inflatable cup.

I need not have worried.

'You've broken your leg,' said Keith.

'*What*?'

'You've broken your leg. You were trying to run away from the fire and tripped on the companionway and broke your leg. We'll have to strap you into a stretcher and lower you over the side.'

Nothing out-of-the-ordinary had happened to entertain the officers for days now, and they set about this task with undisguised relish.

'You're not supposed to *move*,' pleaded Jimmy, pinning me down.

A canvas stretcher was unrolled and I was lifted on to it, Jimmy taking my starboard and the First Mate my port side.

'Careful now. Care-ful,' shouted Keith.

The Lecky took the rope and wrapped it around the stretcher and me.

'Make sure she's secure. Don't want her to drop out. Can't take any risks with that leg.'

I lay on the stretcher, unable to move any of my limbs, incapacitated by the ropes and the Mae West which rose up before me in two orange mountains and blocked off any sight of my feet.

Keith ordered Quist to release the wire, and the lifeboat swung out from the deck and over the sea. I was lying suspended between Jimmy at my head and John at my tail, who were holding the stretcher.

'That's far enough,' said Keith. 'Now, over the side.'

Then everyone began to act very strangely. Jimmy at my head started jigging up and down on the spot. John at my feet followed suit, although less enthusiastically. Keith threw one of his legs up into the air as if to leap over the deckrail and into the lifeboat, let the leg dangle there for a few seconds, then retrieved it back on board. Steve did the same with his long thin left leg, shook it a little in mid-air, then replaced it next to his equally long thin right.

'Right, over with her,' shouted Jimmy, and the stretcher and I were swung into the air. I could see the lifeboat suspended just below me. Beneath that the waves licked at the rust on the hull.

It seemed as if I watched an ocean wash our sides before Jimmy and John swung me back in.

Then I realised. We were only *pretending* to abandon ship. Everyone, that is, except the Old Man, who didn't ever pretend, and still stood stoically on his bridge.

'All right, back to work,' ordered Keith.

Jimmy unwound my ropes.

'Enjoy that?' he beamed.

'No. Not particularly.'

'How did you like my impression of running along the deck as a
stretcher bearer?'

'Not much.'

'Well someone has to get injured every boat drill. We have to
practise lowering the stretcher over the side.'

'But why did it have to be me?'

Jimmy thought this was the funniest thing he had heard all day,
perhaps for several days. Making fun of me was a welcome relief
from the worry of the approaching land and what it might bring. If
for no other, that was a good reason for having me on board.

I thought of tackling Jimmy over the wedding rumours, but
decided against it. It would be better not to raise the matter.

'By the way,' he called back along the deck. 'Why don't you ever
make yourself look *pretty*?'

Everything had turned topsy turvy. While the ship had grown in
proportion well beyond her true size – so that the bow and the
accommodation block at the stern seemed as far apart as two cities
– the land outside had shrunk. Within a day we skipped from one
end of Portugal to the other with the ease of taking a stroll across a
local park. By the next morning we had rounded Cape Finisterre,
took a bearing from Cabo Torinana light, crossed over the ten-
thousand-foot-deep Theta Gap in the ocean floor, and entered the
Bay of Biscay. The 'terrible Bay' was as flat as a puddle. The
officers had been full of dire warnings about the violent baptism I
was about to receive. They had their own word for it, to be
'biscayed'. I had been looking forward to a jarring, more pronounced movement of the ship instead of this slothful rolling. But
we swung through the Bay with the same soporific motion that we
had been travelling along at for the last week. It was as unpleasant as being constantly doped up with Avloclor, and just as
nauseous.

The atmosphere on board was also sleepy, with nothing to look
forward to. The officers had talked of the 'Channel fever' which
often struck men as they left the Bay. The symptoms were nervous
twitching and irritability, and the cause was excitement at the
prospect of soon reaching your destination and going on shore
leave. Everyone on the *Minos* must have been inoculated against
'the Channels', as there was no evidence of any cases on board.

The colder it grew outside, the more insular we became, and the doors out to the deck were seldom opened. We walked up to the bridge, down to the bar, through to the mess and up to our cabins again in slow motion, passing each other on the companionways.

'All right?'

'All right. You all right?'

'All right.' And the brief encounter was over.

Only the Captain remained unaffected by the weather and the proximity of Britain, but then he wasn't leaving the ship.

'Nineteen-year-old Aberdonian lass,' he began. 'Padre's daughter. Disappeared. Just like that. In India. Never heard anything of her again.'

The Old Man's murderous tales had seemed surreal in the ocean. But as we approached British shores, they became menacing. We would soon be on land where, as the Captain pointed out to us each morning, these sort of atrocities were committed with horrific frequency. Breakfasts were terrifying reminders of the dangers we were all about to face.

Our minds were further agitated by the 1230 message. We would not be sailing into Liverpool after all, Keith announced, but Tilbury. Liverpool was on strike.

'But Karen's changed the sheets!' cried Tim, outraged. 'She'll have to change them again now!'

Responding to the sluggish water and mental state of the men, the ship decreased speed. The closer we drew to Britain, the slower we ran, until we crawled into the English Channel as if ashamed of being there at all.

'See. Visibility disappears just like that,' said the Captain as I walked on to the bridge, as if he were our own King Canute commanding the clouds to draw around us. The sky was murky and dull, and England was still hiding behind the grey haze.

The Channel is one of the most dangerous waterways in the world. Narrowing down to less than twenty nautical miles, great bulkers squeeze through this opening on their way north. Charts of wrecks in the English Channel are published for electrical and water companies for use when digging cables into the seabed. The water is black with dots, from HMS *Windsor Castle*, stranded on the Goodwin Sands in 1693, to the case of the British general cargo vessel *Niceto de Larrinaga* and the French oil tanker *Sitala* which, in 1961, collided in the fog with the loss of two lives.

As we edged gingerly along, out from the haze would emerge the silhouette of a tanker, huge and menacing, lying low across the water like a floating pontoon. It made the 21,000 ton *Minos* seem like a precocious young dinghy, and we would dodge in and out of her path, furiously signalling at the unwieldy giant as we flitted around her like a fly annoying an elephant taking a leisurely bath.

A large tanker travelling at twenty knots can take over forty miles to come to a halt, twice the breadth of the Channel itself. A ship the tonnage of the *Minos* has a stopping distance of about ten miles. If two ships are on a collision course in poor visibility, by the time they see each other with the naked eye an accident is often unavoidable.

This is a shipmaster's worst nightmare: he is standing on his bridge looking out at a vessel with which he knows his ship is going to collide, and yet he can do very little about it. His instinct, and his instructions, are to take evasive action by altering course to starboard. Although it is too late to avoid collision, he hopes the approaching vessel might just scrape his port quarter and cause minimal damage.

Once a collision is inevitable, however, the most sensible and life-preserving course of action is to aim straight for the bow of the oncoming ship. An end-on, bow-to-bow collision between two streamlined vessels may result in no more than a glancing blow. The tips of their bows could, with luck, skim off one another. But if the captain orders a sharp turn, he exposes the broadside to the oncoming vessel. In the event of a collision, his ship would receive a mighty gash in her side and probably go down.

An experienced eye had to be kept on the *Minos*'s radar, and the Captain was frequently to be found pacing before the console and staring out in to the Channel. The atmosphere on the bridge changed. It became a command centre on constant alert. No one came up to hang around by the kettle any more, and Billy was officious.

'Hi. How's things?' I said as I came up on Dogs, and the Third Mate flinched. The Old Man stood with his back as rigid as a board, looking out through his binoculars. With his eyes pressed so tightly to the glass that they puffed out at the sides, he quoted:

'This City now doth, like a garment, wear
The beauty of the morning; silent, bare,
Ships, towers, domes, theatres, and temples lie
Open unto the fields, and to the sky;
All bright and glittering in the smokeless air.

'Who wrote that?' he barked.
  'Don't know, sir.'
'Wordsworth. Wordsworth's Westminster Bridge. Wordsworth
wrote that.' And he brought his binoculars down to his waist in one
sharp movement, and marched from the bridge.
    I imagined the Captain's binoculars had pierced through the oily
haze and all the way up the Thames Estuary to London.

As we made our way up the English Channel, we reduced speed
more and more. Sometimes it felt as if we weren't moving at all, we
were so smothered by the silence of the fog. On board it was as if the
seamen were mentally packing, gathering together the language of
the ship and storing it at the back of their minds, as I had stored
Africa in the cupboard in my cabin. Talk in the bar was about our
ETA and the next voyage, but there wasn't really much talk at all.
The video was switched on earlier than usual, and we watched
three films in one night. There were no more parties planned by
Jimmy.
    On the day before we were due at Tilbury, the fog was so thick
that you couldn't see the derricks from the bridge. We had crossed
from the western to the eastern hemisphere for the second time on
the voyage, turning right back on ourselves. It was quite cold on
deck. There had been no water in the pool for several days now. I
was wearing lots of clothes against the chilly wind and felt as if I
was being suffocated. Instead of squatting in the tub and pouring
water over myself West African style or taking a shower, I had a
bath to warm me up and thought I was drowning.
    Now far away from Africa and shrouded from Britain by the fog,
the seamen retreated back into talking about the past, the safest
country they knew, and the one in which they were happiest. This
once, the Captain joined in the officers' games, and became
expansive.
    'Pity. Lots of the old traditions are dying off. Just don't have the

men any more,' he said. 'At eight in the morning the captain used to blow three whistles and the four flags were raised. At sunset he blew three whistles and they were lowered. Now where would you get the men from to do it? The flag is sometimes up sometimes down now, no one cares.'

I went out on deck. The red ensign fluttered from the stern. The early fog had cleared into a muted midday and the Channel was rippled like a freshly mowed lawn. The tide ebbed, to port some mudbanks curved out of the water like giant seaslugs, and I saw England for the first time.

Part III

Leaving The Ship

Chapter Sixteen

Southend Deepwater Anchorage

LATITUDE 51°30′ NORTH, LONGITUDE 0°53′ EAST

Through the murky early hours we crept along the Kent coast, taking bearings from the lighthouses. The lookout was changed every hour; it was bitterly cold outside, and a keen eye had to be kept on the water, especially in this fog. Our course changed frequently as we followed the curves of a coastline we could not see. Fog horns roared out into the still night, crying, 'Is anybody there?'

Yambasu was on lookout when I went up on the bridge. I walked outside on to the bridge wing and stood next to him. He was wrapped in an enormous black raincoat reaching to just above his ankles, with a huge hood and a scarf wrapped about his neck. Somewhere inside was buried his face, but I couldn't see it. I only knew it was Yambasu because I had read that he was on lookout in the Deck Log. Perhaps it was another one of the sailors standing in for him, and not even the Mate would know.

Since sharing a bowl of chicken pepper soup between Tema and Monrovia, I had never been alone with the crew, and I hadn't really spoken to them at all. I had given Abu and Mohammed my order from the menu at dinner, and sometimes a few words would be bounced between the stewards and the officers around the white tablecloths. There may well have been members of the crew whom I had never even seen, particularly those who worked in the engine room, and there were those whose names I didn't know, even though I recognised their faces. Even when I did know what one of the Sierra Leonean crew was called, it was because I had heard him being given orders by one of the officers, or read his name in the Deck Log. We were never introduced.

It was bitterly cold on lookout that night, the fog falling like a chill over the ship. I hunched up to keep myself warm and muttered, 'Brrrr, freezing,' to Yambasu.

The great raincoat didn't move, but kept looking straight ahead into the fog. Perhaps there was no one inside there at all.

'Brrrrrr,' I said again. 'It must get really cold out here.'

A black hand appeared from out of a deep pocket, and pulled the hood even further over the hidden face.

'Don't you get cold?' I asked.

It was a ridiculous question. Of course the lookout got cold. But I was trying to talk to Yambasu as two people might who meet in a street and don't know each other very well. I was trying to make it clear that I wasn't going to issue him an order, like the officers did, or talk down to him. I just wanted to make conversation, as equals.

'You from Freetown?' I asked. 'Never been there. But I'd like to. I only got as far north as Togo.'

There was no reply.

Then, 'Very cold,' said Yambasu, whose face I still hadn't seen. 'Very cold.'

The voice told me that he wanted me to go away. I was served with the British officers at dinner every night, and I drank with them in the officers' saloon. It was no good pretending to be friendly with the crew, just because I had spent some time in West Africa.

'Very cold,' said Yambasu again, as if I was responsible for his suffering from the bitter weather. 'Very cold . . . Master.'

He turned round towards me. From deep inside the hood, two white eyes looked straight out from a stern black face. Yambasu was old enough to be my father, perhaps older still. He slowly turned his face away, and looked out to sea.

By the middle of Morning watch, the sun was engaged in a desperate battle to break through the solid blanket of cloud. Yesterday the cloud had won, and for eight long hours it had felt as if we had had to push ourselves through the soupy air. Today it seemed the sun might be in with a chance, for already low over the horizon there was a tinge of colour other than grey.

A sentry of seagulls escorted us in to the Thames Estuary. At first there was just one, swooping in a long low arc across the stern. Then another arrived, and one took the port, the other the starboard beam. Then there were three, and they flew in no particular pattern but kept close hauled to our sides.

By 1030 hours we were at anchor in eleven fathoms of oily water, and the pilot, considering us now safe, buzzed away in his tiny launch and was swallowed up by the fog.

We stayed swathed in this stillness, cocooned by the fog and swinging gently on our anchor in the light wind, for two days. The clocks were adjusted half an hour, so at last we were in sync with the British Isles. The weather did not clear, and we seldom saw the land that was less than a mile away. The only indication of where we were came from the words typed at the top of Jimmy's white menu cards – 'Off Southend'. There was just one other small clue to our location, recorded in the Deck Log. For the first time there was a new type of entry: 'Drizzle'.

As my arrival back in Britain was weeks behind schedule, I asked Doug if I could let someone know when we were due through his radio. A phone link could be made via the operator on land.

I called Liam. It was a strained conversation.

'We're coming into fucking Tilbury, not Liverpool,' I said, determined to deliver the message with no frills, just relaying the facts.

'Good. That's much more convenient. I'll come and collect you.'

'Fucking strike,' I began to explain.

'What?'

'Fucking strike in Liverpool.'

'Oh.'

There were a few moments of nothing but hisses and crackles.

'Are you all right?' he said.

'Of course I'm bloody all right.'

'It's just, you're swearing more than you usually do.'

'Am I?'

There was another awkward, though barely perceptible, silence.

'Looking forward to seeing you, honey,' he said.

'Me too,' I gabbled. 'Got to go. Bye.'

Doug was standing outside as I left the radio room, and his lips were pursed.

'You know everyone can hear you?' he hissed.

'Where?'

'On the radio. It's an open channel. Anyone can listen in. You're not supposed to use bad language. There's a strict code.'

'Why didn't you tell me?'

'I thought you'd know. You've been here long enough. You ought to know.'

Doug spoke slowly, pronouncing each word distinctly to control his rage. I had not acted like a proper seaman ought to act. The officers swore like blazes, but only in the bar. There was a place for everything on this ship, including the use of the word 'fuck'.

The last night in the officers' saloon was sombre, like an inner-city pub long after five o'clock when all the office workers have run home to the suburbs and only a few hard-drinking regulars remain, who have nothing much left to say to each other which they haven't said many times before. We pretended we would be sailing together again soon on the next voyage. No addresses were exchanged, no telephone numbers swapped, because we were all so certain we would meet up in two months' time. For Jimmy there would be no next voyage, but even Jimmy seemed to have forgotten this, and talked about where he might go and who the Old Man might be. Tomorrow night, the officers would be sitting in their local pub and going home to sleep in a house. But there was no mention of that either.

It was unlikely that the officers would bother to get in touch with each other during their two months' shore leave. Friendships are geographically tied, and where you have met and grown to know someone is often more important than for how long. Nobody thinks of a ship as a geographical location; a ship is thought of as something which travels *between* geographical locations, whereas in fact she doesn't travel at all. Wherever you are on board a ship, you are always in the same country.

Friendships on board were anchored in that country in which they had been spawned. When they left the ship, the men would become less than acquaintances to each other.

I settled my account at the bar, and bought the men a box of Special Strength Skol. I immediately regretted it. They each came over to thank me with genuine gratitude, and it made me feel ashamed. The beer was such a trivial return for their kindness, and it would have been better to have given nothing at all.

Billy's exam results had come through, and our Third Mate was now a certificated Master Mariner. We celebrated mildly, but strayed back to our own quarters earlier than usual. Through in the cabin next door, I could hear the lullaby of the BBC World Service, the announcer's voice paced and reassuring. Even off Southend, where he could have tuned into the local and national radio stations, the Captain listened to the familiar sound of the World Service – just as he had off Douala. The West Coast of Africa and the south-east coast of England were all the same to the Old Man, for he was still on his ship.

I packed my clothes back into the tin trunks. My cabin was tidier than it had been for weeks, but there would be no more inspections. Whatever the Old Man thought of my orderliness, it was too late to change it now.

There was a knock at the door. It was the Captain, and for a moment I hoped he might be making a last-minute inspection, and my reputation as a shipshape seaman could be saved. He handed me a small piece of flimsy white paper headed Steering Certificate.

'I think you've earned this,' he said, and marched off next door. It was the last in a bizarre catalogue of gifts the Captain had given me – a half-page history of the *Minos*, out of date newspapers, a verdigrised brass passenger plate – and by far the most precious.

When I heard the Captain's front door click a short while later, I knew he was going up on the bridge to check on Billy. As we heaved anchor just past midnight, swung to starboard, and edged along the River Thames to Tilbury, there were two qualified captains staring out across our bow.

Chapter Seventeen

West Africa Terminal, Tilbury

LATITUDE 51°28′ NORTH, LONGITUDE 0°23′ EAST

The sun didn't rise over Tilbury the next morning, it just listlessly washed a vapid yellow about the sky. The view from the deck was much like that of any other dock before the day's work begins, the concrete perspiring with dew. But Tilbury remained like this as the day grew lighter; there were no boys balancing trays of mangoes on their heads, no hawkers shouting 'Hey, Sparky!' up to the deck, no card-playing in the shadow of the ship, and no Mr Alhaji Moham-med Said strolling down the wharf with his leather pouches of ivory bangles when the news spread that a ship was in. The sinister stillness hung over us all morning, with just the crashes and creaks of the cranes screaming along the quay.

Offloading began early. The billets of wood from Douala were lifted off and the bags of cocoa beans from Tema came out of the belly of the ship. It was as if our guts were being ripped out. Soon we would be a hollow, tinny beast with the officers and cargo all gone. Only the Old Man, alone in his cabin or pacing the bridge, and the Kru seamen would remain on board waiting on orders for the next voyage.

I stood at the top of the gangway and waited for the visitors.

Karen was the first to arrive. She drove up in a zippy little white sports car and emerged legs first from its low slung front seat. The Second had been quite right, she was pretty and did look kind of Swedish, or how you would imagine a Swedish woman to look, with a wholesome open face and a long bob of thick blonde hair protecting it like a helmet. She exuded healthiness – there was nothing sneaky or sly about Karen – and before she even reached the gangway the officers adored her.

They cackled around her in the bar, offering all their best wishes for the forthcoming baby, of which Karen's strong, shapely body showed no physical evidence whatsoever. But it was an excuse for the men to give her a congratulatory kiss. Kissing appears a very bizarre activity when you have been away from places where people do that sort of thing for a while, as if someone is about to take a bite out of someone else's cheek. I wanted to run up and throw my arms out to protect Karen's wholesome face from being mutilated by the men, imagining a scarlet trickle running past the corner of her perfect pink mouth and splashing in teardrops of blood on to the carpet.

Jimmy approached me as I sat alone in the corner.

'What are you wearing?' he spat, furious.

I was tired of Jimmy's comments about my appearance.

'What does it look like I'm wearing? A dustbin liner?'

'Yes. Except a dustbin liner would be more attractive,' he snapped back.

I had agonised over how I should appear in front of Liam and, after unpacking everything from my tin trunks again, settled for a pair of beige canvas jeans and a baggy grey sweatshirt. The jeans had grown too tight and gripped me in a vice between the crotch.

'You can't meet your fella like that,' protested Jimmy.

'Why the hell not?'

'Because you look like a bleeding fella.'

Jimmy was rigid with rage, but he was angry not with me but with himself. He had behaved impeccably towards me, like a proper gent, as had all the men. Yet I had come on board a young Englishwoman in a flowery sundress and was leaving the *Minos* a scruffy, sexless thing. Somehow I had turned into somebody Jimmy would be ashamed to be seen walking along the street with in Liverpool. As far as Jimmy was concerned, he and the other officers had done me a great disservice.

'What the hell will your fella think of us?' he said, 'when you turn up like that.'

I stood at the gangway and stared out at the concrete quay until a tidy little red car turned the corner and drove towards the ship. The curly-headed man in my photograph was at the wheel. He looked up at me from the dock, a mop of hair with two tiny feet sticking out at the bottom of it, and waved.

'Come on up,' I shouted.

The invitation sounded as if it were made by a voice other than my own, and when we hugged it was as if I was watching someone else hugging him.

'You look good. You've put on weight,' Liam said.

'Yep. Come on in. I'll show you my cabin.'

We walked along the alleyway.

'How was it? Any problems?' he asked.

'Nope.'

Liam laughed. 'Are you only going to speak to me in monosyllables or what?'

We sat next to each other on the bed where I had dreamt with *The White Hotel*. I saw my cabin through his eyes, a square room decorated in a dated orange with a bedside table, desk, and fitted cupboard, all in imitation wood-vinyl, and a plain white bathroom to one side. It was as unmemorable as a room in a cheap motel chain.

'How was Africa?' He had obviously dismissed the voyage as a topic unlikely to produce any interesting conversation.

'Lovely. Great.'

'Did you get sick?'

'No. Not really.'

'It's comfy in here. Bit like a hotel.'

'Umm. I suppose so.'

He reached over to touch me. 'Dea . . . '

'Let's go for a drink.'

In the officers' saloon we sat away from the rest of the men. Jimmy, leaning against the bar, waved over to me and I wiggled my fingers back at him. The sun was barely over the yardarm, yet the men were already getting merry. The arrival of the creature 'woman' on board, in the wonderful form of Karen, was something to be celebrated. I wondered what these middle-aged officers in their blues uniform looked like to the man sitting next to me.

'Good bunch?' he said cheerily, determined to like them for my sake.

'Yeah. A good bunch.'

'Why don't you introduce me to a couple of them? What about that bloke telling the stories at the bar? Who's he?'

I looked over to Jimmy. He was off the wagon, and Karen was his only rival in gaining the officers' attention.

'He's the Chief Steward. It's his last voyage.'

'Retiring?'

'No. He's been made redundant.'

I knocked back my Special Strength Skol, slammed the can down on the table with the rim around the edge, heaved myself up from the low-backed swivel chair, and announced, 'Let's go.'

As we walked down the gangway, empty containers were being hoisted from the holds on cranes. As I walked towards the car, my legs swayed beneath me and I was worried I might faint. I thought I must be overcome with emotion, and determinedly strode out for the car. It was only later that I realised I had been suffering from sea legs.

Steve came down the gangway behind us with an Adidas bag slung over his shoulder, as if making his way home from a football match on Saturday afternoon.

'Look after her!' he called across to Liam as I got into the passenger seat, and winked at me.

I nodded at the guard at the iron gate – 'I've come from the *Minos*' – and we drove away from the dock, until the ship looked so small.

Chapter Eighteen

Home

LATITUDE 51°30′ NORTH, LONGITUDE 0°05′ WEST

Life on land seemed very dull. I tried to keep up my log for a while, but there was nothing to record, so the entries soon stopped.

Life on land also seemed absolutely absurd. The telephone crouched like a rabid cat in the corner of the sitting room, every now and then screeching violently. When the phone rang in my cabin, it could only have been one of the officers. This phone brought all sorts of mad people into my home.

It rang again.

'Miss Birkett?'

'Yes.'

'Good morning, Miss Birkett. I'm from Bright White Rainbow Discount Windows. I'm calling about a superb offer which I'm sure you will be interested in. We're offering two windows, double glazed PVC frames, for the price of one. Our representative . . .'

'No, thank you.'

'Have you been considering a conservatory?'

I looked through the window of my second-floor flat over the inner city building site. It had been drizzling all afternoon.

'No.'

The salesman was very persistent and started to read his script more quickly, with no pauses at all for punctuation.

'Here at Bright White Rainbow Discount Windows we are making a superb offer I'm quite sure will interest you we have many satisfied customers in your area when would it be convenient for our representative . . .'

'Where did you get my name from?'

'The phone book.' The salesman sounded almost apologetic. 'We go through the phone book.'

I hung up.

I went for a walk along the south bank of the River Thames from Southwark Bridge to Waterloo. The tide was low, and the muddy bottom sucked up the concrete walls built to keep the water from flowing over into the city. The riverbed was littered with domestic objects – the metal skeleton of a pram, the pink plastic foot of a child's doll, a sodden slipper, a dead dog – as if some family home up-river in the suburbs had been washed away by the tide and was being carried towards the sea. I picked up the doll's foot and put it in my pocket.

A pleasure boat slid under Blackfriars Bridge on its way to the Tower. I could hear the skipper instructing the tourists to look to the left for a fine view of St Paul's Cathedral. Apart from the hum of the traffic on the road which followed the north bank and the broken sound from the loudspeaker on the boat, the river was quiet. Once it would have been the busiest part of the city, known as the First Port of Empire, where lighters, barges and short-sea vessels offloaded sand, tea, wool, indigo, shells, perfume, spices and flour to the warehouses. Now the few barges take waste from the offices in the city. The noisiest form of transport to use the river is not boats, but helicopters, whose airspace across London is restricted to the path of the Thames.

A bench by the river is one of the few places where it is still possible to sense that London was once a great imperial city. For centuries the capital's finest architectural monuments were all constructed along the banks of the Thames: the Tower of London, the Houses of Parliament, the Royal Naval College at Greenwich. Most people travelled through town along the river, so it was from the water that the city should be seen at its best.

Across the river the massive dome of St Paul's rose above the grey layers of an office block, refusing to be cut off from the water. A man sitting on the bench a few feet away from mine, wearing a heavy brown overcoat and black-rimmed glasses, flicked up the corners of his mouth in a faint smile. He fumbled around under his overcoat, pulled out a shrivelled grey penis through the gap between two leather buttons, and began to masturbate. He continued to smile stupidly, as if paying me a great compliment. The Captain was right, land was a very dangerous place indeed.

On the way back home I stopped in a newsagent's and bought a copy of *Singles* magazine. *Singles* is to lonely people what *Autotrader* is to cars or *Gun Mart* to pistols – a weekly forum for their sale. Advertisements sum up a prospective partner's essential and most attractive characteristics within the confines of an inch-square black-edged box. The age, condition ('sprightly', 'young at heart', 'mature', and even 'well-preserved'), and number of previous owners ('divorced', 'once married', 'separated') are given.

One advertisement read:

MERCHANT NAVY Petty Officer, youthful 60, retired from sea, wishes to meet lady, for outings, mutual pleasures, maybe lasting relationship. Colour/nationality immaterial. Box 73024.

There was immense pride in those two words in capital letters at the top of Box 73024 – MERCHANT NAVY. But there was also a sad inevitability about their appearance in this magazine. It could have been Jimmy, if the address hadn't been 'Essex – but will travel'. Jimmy had been married twice; neither marriage had lasted. The Old Man had stayed single, wedded to his ship. It is difficult for a seaman to sustain a relationship on land.

There is an enormous gulf between a seaman's working- and home-life, and it is near impossible to explain to someone who has never been to sea what it is like. Whenever I mentioned how I had come home, the topic of conversation was soon changed. People were interested in talking about Africa, but not the ship. Yet as far as I was concerned, the ship was the far more fascinating country.

I met a woman who was a poet, with a mass of flame red hair which she continually tossed from side to side and played with, making buns and bunches as we talked.

'I couldn't bear it,' she said. 'Just the same sea every day for weeks.'

I launched into my well-rehearsed defence.

'It's not the same at all,' I said enthusiastically. She was a poet and might understand. 'It changes all the time. There's sunrise and sunset, the weather to look out for, and the night sky. There's always something to watch. There are passing ships. Then there are dolphins and . . . '

'Dolphins?' She perked up and stopped playing with her hair. 'Tell me about the dolphins.'

I always mentioned the dolphins, and the reaction was always the same. At last I was beginning to talk about something interesting.

When a landsman's mind ponders on the ocean, it often conjures up romantic visions of dolphins. They are said to be as intelligent as human beings, and to talk to each other. I had watched a television documentary about an American psychic who claimed to be possessed by dolphins, and made dolphin-like noises to prove it. He said that dolphins are just the vessels that beings from other planets use to inhabit while visiting earth. The psychic was very astute in pinpointing a widely held view: dolphins don't really belong in the sea at all. I found myself telling stories of dolphin spottings over and over again – what they looked like, how often we saw them, how they behaved, and the lone dolphin that followed the ship on the starboard quarter.

I had a friend whose mother had been a stewardess on the Liverpool liners, and arranged to see her, hoping she would understand. I told her about the officers, trusting her to be able to see through their brash talk to the sensitive men underneath. Sitting in a high-class London restaurant, she began to remember her mother's time at sea.

'Hated everything foreign,' she said, tucking into lapin aux pruneaux. 'She's living proof that travel narrows the mind.'

It is not only the difficulties in communicating a life at sea which makes shore-based relationships so rocky. The long periods of absence inevitably breed doubts and jealousies. My own love affair had to weather these same nagging questions. I had been on my own with a boatload of men. He had been alone in a capital city teeming with attractive women.

But it was more than just being sexually faithful; I had fallen in love with the sea, and it was as if I had chosen to live in a different country. I didn't try to banish the sea from my land life. I took refuge in it. I pursued anything at all touched with the sea. I walked up and down the river, collecting strange objects of domestic debris washed up on the tide as if trying to reconstruct a home from them.

I went to a meeting of the Watch Ashore, an organisation of Merchant Navy officers' wives. The London branch gathered once a month over luncheon in the Merchant Navy Hotel.

Watch Ashore's aims were 'To stimulate public interest in all matters concerning the Merchant Navy and its officers, and to enlist public support for the reforms which were urgently necessary.' Behind the entirely appropriate activities of Garden Whist Drives, Knitting Parties, Easter Bonnet Competitions and luncheon at the Merchant Navy Hotel, the lady members plotted how to raise funds to promote the cause of the merchant seaman.

Over our roast chicken, the wives talked of their time at sea 'when they allowed wives to sail with their husbands.' Now most of their spouses served on foreign-flagged ships. 'Have to take anything you can get now.'

'Who's your husband with?' someone asked me.

'Well . . . ' and I was saved by the waitress shouting out, 'Hands up those for jam roly poly.'

We exchanged addresses after pudding, and soon a pamphlet arrived in the post – a short history of Watch Ashore published privately for the membership. One chapter was headed, 'WAR – AND AN UNGRATEFUL PEACE', and the last, 'THE FUTURE?'

I made an appointment to visit the head of the Merseyside Mission to Seamen, Reverend Canon Ken Peters. I mumbled something over the phone about writing a book about a sea voyage . . . wanting to talk to the Canon about the decline of shipping in Liverpool . . . hoping to include a section about the Merseyside Mission . . . perhaps he could give me a few leads. But what I really wanted was confession. Perhaps where my friends, lover and a poet had failed me, Canon Peters might understand.

I took a train from London to Liverpool Lime Street, then another train out to Waterloo on the edge of town and close by the Seaforth Container Terminal where those vessels which still call at Liverpool come in to dock.

The port used to be in the centre of town. It *was* the centre of town from where, as in Douala, the seamen could walk ashore. Now Canon Peters drives in his little minibus with a flashing orange light on the roof to visit ships and offer a lift to any seamen who wish to use the Mission's facilities.

The Mission's headquarters was a detached building set off a main road. The bar was even more cavernous than the officers' saloon on the *Minos*, and much more dreary, with the most enormous TV screen I had ever seen. Canon Peters said it was the biggest on the market.

The Canon was a kind and confident man who, when not behind the wheel of his sirened minibus, drove a family saloon with two car seats for children strapped in the back. He offered me lunch near-by, and the journey from the Merseyside Mission to the hotel was an exhausting one for the Canon, for he insisted on opening every door we came across – the door from the Mission headquarters, the car door, the door into the hotel, the door into the hotel bar – scuttling in front of me every time a door presented itself before us, which was often. I began to feel uncomfortable; I wanted him to slap me on the back and greet me as a sailor returned from the sea. Instead he was treating me like a gentleman would a young lady he hardly knew, which, however loath I was to admit it, was what we really were.

I ordered a Home Cooked Ham Sandwich and the Canon went for the vegetable curry. He set about explaining his work to me, as if I was a complete stranger to matters concerning the sea. There was never any question, the Canon said, of him preaching when he visited a ship; he just offered the services of the Mission building to the seamen – money-changing facilities, a non-denominational chapel where a Muslim is free to unroll his prayer mat or a Christian confess to his god, sightseeing tours of Liverpool, and the dreary bar with its giant TV screen.

'The only thing that gives a sign that I'm of the church is this,' said the Canon, and he tapped his dog collar. It made a strange hollow sound, as if he had hit an empty biscuit tin.

The Mission's work, he explained, was now mostly with seamen from overseas whose ships were docked in Liverpool. Multi-national crews – the Canon had known of up to nineteen nationalities on one vessel – were now the norm, and communication problems rife. The Mission would be called in to settle disputes and act as an arbitrator between two parties.

What about African seamen who had settled in Liverpool, I asked?

'Tribal, very tribal,' said the Canon.

I asked if he still had much contact with Liverpool seamen.

'Oh yes,' he said. 'Every three weeks or so I scatter ashes, about eight lots every time, on the Mersey.'

He drove me back into town along the Regent Road. To our right was the broad river, but we couldn't see it for the piles of coal and ugly half-empty sites where what remained of the cargoes and old rusting containers were stored. The Canon tried to transform this urban dereliction into a picture of prosperity and promise.

'Some local residents do complain about the dust from the coal,' he confessed. 'But if you take away the coal because of the dust, if you take away the animal feed because of the smell, if you take away the scrap metal because of the noise, if you take away the timber because of the rainforest, then what is left of Liverpool?'

Later that night I visited the district known as Liverpool 8, where many of Liverpool's black people live. Eight per cent of the city's dwindling population is black – the oldest black community in Britain – with many descendants from West African seamen and some former seamen themselves.

The main street, Princes Road, roared with cars rushing through on their way out to the suburbs or the airport. Rows and rows of terraced houses, and occasionally blocks of flats, arched off on either side. There was evidence of the Canon's 'tribalism' all over Liverpool 8. Doors advertised the Sierra Leone Club, the Gambia Club, the Liberian Association, and the Ibo Club.

I could see no lights on at the Ibo Club, and loudly rattled a huge door which I was convinced would be locked. It swung open. From inside the small reception area, I could see why I had thought the building was deserted and dark. Sheets of plywood were nailed over the spaces where windows should have been.

The reception area contained no furniture at all, and was boxed in on all sides by flimsy walls. In one of the walls there was a battered plywood door with a small iron grill to one side. Above the grill someone had scrawled on the wall in black felt tip pen:

MEMBERS ONLY ONE POUND ADMISSION FRIDAY AND
SATURDAY KEEP QUIET

Through the other side of the grill I could see a light was on, and I could hear two men talking and the soft tap-tap of pool being played.

I shouted, 'Hello!', but no one replied.

I shouted 'Hello!' again, but there was still no response. I rattled the plywood door, but it must have been bolted from the inside.

I stood in the reception area for ten minutes or more, shouting 'Hello!' through the grill and rattling the door. If I hollered loud enough they had to let me in. I became convinced that on the other side I would find the acceptance I was seeking. I imagined there would be an old Kru seaman, propped up against a bar, wanting to tell me about his life. I saw myself as some sort of messenger from one world to another. I was on a mission far higher than the Reverend Canon Ken Peters'.

But as the door remained bolted and my shouts unheard, my vision began to fade. I no more belonged in the Ibo Club than I had amongst the Kru on the lower bridge deck, and I was trespassing. I was a nosy, interfering intruder, and I should go back to where I belonged, wherever that might be.

On the street outside, three women shuffled past in purdah, their cloth wrapped around and around. It seemed very sensible wear in the bitter early evening air.

Back in London, I ordered the *Africa Pilot* in the British Library, to read about the hazardous ruined jetties in Lagos Lagoon.

'I used to be a deck officer,' the young man behind the counter said in a southern European accent, handing me the large blue book.

'Who with?'

'Mavrolean Brothers.' He spelt it for me.

'You Spanish?'

'Greek. People here always think I'm Spanish.'

I flinched at the word 'Greek'. Here, over a library counter, was my first face-to-face meeting with the corner-cutting, untrustworthy, horrible Greeks.

'Why did you leave the sea?' I asked politely.

'Colour blind.' He began, 'I went to sea at sixteen, as an uncertificated third mate. After four years I went for the statutory course at King Edward's College. They gave me a lantern test. I failed. I took it six times altogether, I just kept going back. Eventually they said they didn't want to see me again.'

'How did that make you feel?' I made a hopeless attempt to be jolly.

'Soul-broken,' he replied.

I stood at the library counter fumbling for words. How the sea 'somehow gets you', how it is 'difficult to get used to working ashore'.

He told me about the three officers he worked with on the four ships he sailed on during his time at sea. All tried to give up and leave the ship; one started a decorating business; one opened a burger bar; the third became a mechanic. The decorating business closed within two months. Within six, all three were back at sea.

The library assistant had left the sea fifteen years ago. He'd heard that deck officers weren't called deck officers any more.

'Deck Managers,' he said. 'Deck Managers!' shaking his dark handsome head. 'Want to go for a drink when I finish? Seeing as we've both got salt in our veins?'

I wrote to all the officers through the Fleet Personnel Department of the shipping line. In reply a card arrived with a picture of a tea clipper on it. 'We are presently loading for the Red Sea,' it read, 'on charter to the Italians. Our ports are Port Sudan, Agaba, Hodeido, Jeddah and a new port called King Fahd Port. Some of your old friends are still here – Tim the Second Engineer, Keith Markham the Second Mate and Billy Kelly the Third Mate. The Africans flew to Freetown from Rotterdam two days ago, all having served one year on board. Perhaps after completion of this hire we may find ourselves loading for Nigeria again.' The card was signed off, 'Steady as she goes, Jim Scott.'

It took me some time to realise who Jim Scott was. He was the Old Man. I had only known him as Captain and it came as a shock to me that he had a full name like everyone else. Jim Scott sounded like a name assumed for the use of landsmen, as an acne-ridden Chinese teenage student I once met called Deng, had adopted the name 'Travis Wiseman' for the convenience of foreigners. As far as I was concerned, Jim Scott was just a pseudonym and 'the Captain' was our commander's real name.

Jimmy, now redundant, replied to my calls only when it was very late and he was very drunk.

'Just wanted to say hello. Do keep *quiet*,' he'd shout into a silent, and obviously empty, room.

'I've got a bit of company,' he'd say as if taking me into his confidence, and click his own full glass against another empty one. 'Can't talk long.'

'Still young enough to pull them.' I colluded in his sad fiction.

'Better go now, she's wanting me,' he'd howl, as if having to bawl over a party. Then hang up.

I wanted to remember Jimmy as the legendary seaman, of whom I could be inordinately proud, so set out to discover more about his Star of Africa which he said William Tubman, the Liberian President until 1971, had awarded him. I called the Liberian Embassy in London and spoke to the Information Officer.

'Could you tell me why President Tubman would have awarded someone the Star of Africa?'

'It is a very elevated award,' the gentleman told me in a slow, reverential tone.

'Who got it?' I asked.

'Freedom fighters for Africa and those who contributed to the liberation struggle.'

This didn't sound right at all. I called the Liberian Desk at the Foreign Office where a woman read from a reference book that the Star of Africa was awarded for 'remarkable distinguished services to Liberia in the field of public service, literature, arts or science', and put me in touch with Europe's leading expert on the history of Liberia.

The Professor had known President William V. Tubman personally.

'I went through his papers at his wife's request when he died,' he said. 'There were piles and piles of blank forms for awarding decorations. Tubman made up all sorts of awards. There was the Knight of the Redemption of Africa, the Grand Third Order of Africa, the Dame Grand Commander of Africa . . . The Order of the Star of Africa was one of those. Tubman loved dishing out medallions.'

'But why would he give one to a Liverpudlian ship's steward?'

The Professor considered my question. 'Tubman hated flying and always travelled by sea if he could. If the steward looked after him it's quite likely that he'd give him a decoration. It's just the sort of thing he would do.'

'The Liberian Embassy told me the Star of Africa was given to African freedom fighters.'

'Good God, no!' exclaimed the Professor. 'Tubman wasn't in the *slightest* bit interested in freedom fighting. He was an old-style politician.'

'Of course, Liberia's changed now,' he added.

The next time I saw Doug's square jaw it was staring at me from a double-page spread in a women's magazine.

THE HORROR OF LIVING NEXT DOOR TO HELL

One day they were just an ordinary family, living in a respectable semi-detached – the next, a gang of axe-wielding Hell's Angels had moved in next door.

Doug had returned to a nightmare. While he had been on the *Minos*, twenty Hell's Angels and a pair of Doberman dogs had moved in next door. They threw axes and fought each other with Samurai swords in the back garden. They flashed at Doug's wife if she looked out of her kitchen window; she heard them discussing a rape. Doug's wife had repeatedly tried to get hold of her husband on the *Minos*, but Doug's radio, which had relayed everyone else's news so reliably, had failed to bring his own. By the time our Radio Officer had arrived back home, his wife and family were living in temporary accommodation for the homeless.

Doug was determined to return to his semi-detached house, his haven on land. On his first night there, barricaded in with an ironing board under the door handle, his Hell's Angels neighbours taunted him, playing 'I Am Sailing, I Am Sailing' over and over again. Then they started banging on the doors and windows, and pulled out a sawn-off shotgun. Doug heard one of them shout, 'We'll kill the bastards!' Doug and his family went into hiding. While they were away, someone broke into their house and slept in their beds. Then Doug was made redundant.

It was unlikely that he would get another job. New ships with more advanced communications systems are no longer legally required to carry a radio officer. The proposed Global Maritime Distress and Safety System (GMDSS) replaces the requirement for radio safety equipment with satcom which does not require a dedicated officer to work it. Other deck officers, with some communications experience, are expected to assume the Sparks's duties.

'Jim Scott' wrote me another card on which 'RADIO OFFICER WAS ON TV CHAT SHOW WITH HIS WIFE' was written in astonished capitals, 'concerning a band of Hippies which had moved in next door.' The Old Man's dire warnings about the land had found yet further confirmation.

His card ended, '*Minos* is up for sale.'

The *Minos* was sold to a Belgian shipping line to replace older tonnage; it seemed the shipping line was selling off its few remaining ships one by one. Renamed, she is now manned by a Belgian crew and never calls at British ports. In my restless attempts to relive something of my time at sea, I called her new owners in Antwerp and asked if I could visit her while she was next docked in Europe. I was prepared to travel to Le Havre, Hamburg, or even Lisbon to see her.

My request was not welcomed by the Belgian Fleet Manager.

'Shipping is a business now,' he told me sternly. 'The glamour days are over.'

Glamour? Who did he think I was? Some flippety young female wanting to visit a boatload of husky sailors and play passenger?

'I know the glamour days are over,' I said in my most calm and businesslike manner. 'That is what I am writing a book about.'

Glamour. This same objection arose again and again whenever I applied to go on board a ship. The shipping company heard a female voice and presumed I was searching for romance – pink gins sipped on deck against a sunset on the high seas in the company of a dashing young uniformed Second Mate.

This presumption came in different disguises.

'It's not like it used to be, you know.'

'I know.'

'We don't take passengers any more.'

'I don't want to be a passenger.'

'You'll be the only woman on board.'

'I've *been* the only woman on board.'

The objections went on and on. No one was as brave as the managing director had been in Apapa. No one else allowed me on board their ship.

I sought out examples of other women who had ventured on to the water which I hoped might bolster my case. But even the very word itself – seawoman – has a false sound about it, and after months of research I had only collected a slim file of cuttings which was not impressive. The *Guardian* newspaper had reported:

Why – *asks Liz Cooke* – are there no women among the 300-plus grinders, trimmers, mastmen, tacticians, navigators and skippers competing in the Indian Ocean for the America's Cup?

Spare Rib published an article on stewardesses, like my friend's mother, who had served on the now extinct luxury liners, and the *Daily Mail* signed up one of its female reporters with the US Navy's aircraft carrier *Lexington* which boasted 150 women amongst its 1350 strong crew. But I couldn't find any reference to women serving on cargo vessels. Then a friend in Nigeria sent me a paragraph from her local newsletter:

Miss Yemisi Adedeji and Mrs O. Fasuyi, two Nigerian marine engineers, have been employed by African Ocean Lines Ltd.

Back in Africa, there seemed to be hope.

Chapter Nineteen

Voyage End

LATITUDE 51°05′ NORTH, LONGITUDE 01°12′ EAST

News of the closure of the shipping line broke slowly. 'CONCERN OVER SHIP SALES' warned the seamen's union *Telegraph* newspaper, and quoted a union official on the fleet: 'It seems to be crumbling before our eyes.'

I received another card from the Captain. He was in command of one of the *Minos*'s sister ships, chartered out to the Japanese and due to be sold on her return to the Far East, from where the Captain would be flown home. 'They're beginning to throw ships away, giving them to the Greeks and all that,' he said. This time he ended, 'What a changed world it is for us.'

The Liverpool newspapers covered the purchase of the shipping line by a foreign shipping giant. But they were buying nothing more than a name. There were no ships left.

The authors of the articles found it impossible to argue against financial facts. Between 1978 and 1986 carryings on the British–West African route had dropped by more than seventy per cent, from 1.6 million to 390,000 freight tonnes. Scheduling with West Africa was unpredictable because of political and economic conditions in the coastal states. But the articles were riddled with nostalgia, and would have fitted more comfortably on the obituaries page, mourning the loss of a dear friend, than amongst the hard business news.

The Captain sent me a newspaper cutting:

ODYSSEY ENDS

They were the stuff that maritime dreams were made of not that many years ago. They were the Liverpool Navy . . . they were the aristos of the ocean, who carried their own insurance and sailed their lovely liners with the attitudes of the Indiamen along purple inked lines etched inflexibly on their charts.

We all know about the persuasive arguments which have swayed the board – a sort of latter-day cradle-to-grave business philosophy that really cannot be faulted.

But you still have to look back with a little sadness to that fleet now sailed off into the sunset . . . sad that the purple inked line on the chart has been drawn firmly and finally into port.

'That,' said the Captain about the purple prose, 'is a fairly accurate summary of recent events.' The vein between West Africa and Britain had been cut.

The Captain got a job as master of a large gas carrier. His new ship had been purchased for sixty-eight million pounds, at a time when an upturn was predicted for British shipping. But the orders had never come in, and she had been laid up idle off the West Coast of Scotland for over ten years. A crew of three were kept on board – a chief engineer, a mate and a master – to look after and service her. As it was costly to open up the accommodation block, designed to house several dozen men, the three officers slept in a Nissen hut on deck. There was very little power on board, and the electronic gyro compasses were switched off. So the Old Man took the noon-day sight with a sextant, and used the same instrument to take bearings from the land. The ship was held down with eleven anchors, but it was possible that, in the stormy seas off the West Coast, she might drag.

When the Captain was on board, the news came through that the gas carrier had been sold. She is now valued at five million pounds scrap.

I spoke to Jim Scott on the phone. He used the personal pronoun, and even, once, chuckled.

'1500 hours,' he said. 'I took the message that she was sold on June 17th, 1500 hours. I took the message myself on the bridge. Funny that.'

In Britain we are all, however little we recognise it, connected with the sea. Our history has been determined by the fact that we are surrounded by water. Our language is awash with the imagery of the sea – pour oil on troubled waters, clear the decks, in the doldrums, all at sea. Ship metaphors are frequently used to describe the arrangement of our society. We still rely almost totally on the water for our imports. Ninety-nine per cent of what we eat, buy and enjoy from abroad is imported by sea. Yet we pretend that the sea has nothing to do with us, not any more.

I decided to move out of London to a place by the water. From where I now live, it is a short walk to the coast of the English Channel. I have a pair of binoculars, and from the top of the cliffs I can watch the ships creep up towards Southend Deepwater Anchorage and down towards the ocean. There are all types of vessels – tankers, bulkers, liners, tramps, trawlers and ferries – from all over the world. Occasionally I spot a multi-purpose break-bulk and container cargo vessel, although she rarely flies the British flag.

When I sit at my desk, I can hear the horn of the ferries giving a short blast before letting go the ropes and sailing for France. It is here I write my letters. One of my most regular correspondents is Peter, my Mount Cameroon guide.

I received a letter folded into the pattern of a pyramid:

Dea

It had been a pleasure reading from you filling this in haste. I'm Peter Bokwe from Buea Cameroon.

I got your letter. The letter interested me to an extend I was of great joy that day.

I want to know the cost of a small working radio for my self.

Now I am in class 7 next year I will complete my school and go to the secondary same as you.

How do you and your journey you made.

Nex time I will write more about myself and my brother.

Its from me.

Peter

I sat down to write my reply:

Peter,

Thank you so much for your letter. I'm Dea Birkett from Folkestone, England.

Then I crossed it out. I began:

Dear Peter,

On the ship they called me Jella . . .

Acknowledgements

There are many people to thank. Most of all, the managing director of the shipping line without whom my voyage, and this book, would never have been; retired Purser James E. Cowden for sharing his knowledge; Captain Graeme Cubbin for his careful reading of the manuscript; Susan Roast for the unenviable task of proofreading in my absence; Agbor Enompagn for correcting me about Cameroon; Reginald Amegatchwer for trying to trace the Accra 'cathedral'; and Mr Ken Birch for his insights into the Liverpool shipping world.

My editor at Gollancz, Georgia Garrett, has been just wonderful.

In West Africa, Jane Bryce, Wendy Pittaway, Josephine Ross, Billy Hawkes, and the late Reverend Mbuk and his family all offered me enormous hospitality and kindness.

I thank the following for answering my queries and sharing their perspectives – Tony Lane, Sue Hargreaves, Richard Woodman, George Deutsch, Clare Thomas, Kevin Toolis, Professor Christopher Clapham, Andrew Thomas, and Mrs Sheila Allen of Watch Ashore.

I would also like to mention the following books, which informed and inspired me:

James E. Cowden and John O.C. Duffy *Elder Dempster Fleet History 1852–1985* (1986)

Ronald Hope (ed.) *The Seaman's World* (London 1982)

Peter Kemp (ed.) *The Oxford Companion to Ships and the Sea* (Oxford 1976)

Tony Lane *Grey Dawn Breaking* (Manchester 1986)

Liverpool. Gateway of Empire (London 1987)

Humphrey Quill *John Harrison. The Man Who Found Longitude* (London 1968)

Richard Woodman *Voyage East* (London 1988)

Further acknowledgements for copyright permissions are due to OUP for Peter Kemp (ed.) *The Oxford Companion to Ships and the Sea*, Victor Gollancz Ltd for D. M. Thomas's *The White Hotel*, *Lloyds List*, the *Seafarer*, and the Controller of Her Majesty's Stationary Office for the *Africa Pilot* (Crown Copyright. Reproduced from Admiralty Publications).